Transmission Lines
Explained

Feeders, Waves, Stubs and
a whole lot more for Radio Amateurs

By Mike Parkin, G0JMI

Published by
Radio Society of Great Britain of 3 Abbey Court, Priory Business Park, Bedford
MK44 3WH, United Kingdom
www.rsgb.org

First Printed 2020

Reprinted Digitally 2023 onwards

ISBN: 9781 9101 9387 7

Cover design: Kevin Williams, M6CYB
Editing: Giles Read, G1MFG
Production: Mark Allgar, M1MPA
Typography and design: Mark Pressland

Printed in Great Britain by 4Edge Ltd of Hockley in Essex

Any amendments or updates to this book can be found at:
www.rsgb.org/booksextra

Contents

Dedication

To my wife Karen, with thanks for her support, help and patience during the last year, while I have been working on this book.

Acknowledgments

I am grateful for the help provided by wife Karen who has kindly proof-read my original draft with the aim of ensuring the text was understandable and for identifying typographical mistakes. Karen says he also learnt a lot about transmission lines too.

My thanks are also passed to Mark Allgar, M1MPA, and to Giles Read, G1MFG, for their encouragement, support and help to me during the writing of this book.

Introduction

A radio station comprises three fundamental components, these being:

- The transceiver and its power supply

- The antenna

- The interconnecting cable between the transceiver and the antenna, which is referred to as the transmission line or feeder cable.

Essentially, the role of the feeder cable is to convey RF power between the transceiver and the antenna for the both transmit and receive modes of operation. Therefore, as a part of this power-transfer role, the efficiency of the feeder cable is essential to the overall operation of the system. This is to ensure that:

- As much of the transmitter's RF power is available for the antenna to radiate as possible

- As much of the RF power received by the antenna is available for the receiver to function successfully.

Fundamentally, a feeder cable purely comprises a pair of conductors which are run in parallel in close proximity to each other. Therefore, for a seemingly straightforward concept, it is surprising how involved some of the aspects associated with transmission lines can be. Consequently, the objective here has been to provide a practical guide to transmission lines and keep the theoretical aspects to a minimum where possible.

1.1 Scope of this Book

The aim of this book is to introduce the use and operation of transmission lines using descriptions to support understanding, rather than through mathematics. However, there are occasions where the mathematics has to be involved and this has been kept to a minimum whenever possible. Where concepts associated with a transmission line have been introduced, these have been supported using examples throughout the book.

A chapter summarising transmission line concepts provides a lead into line parameters including characteristic impedance, loss, velocity factor and the propagation constant. This sets the basis for a chapter describing how a mismatch, between the transmission line and its termination load (eg antenna), can give rise to reflections which allow a standing wave pattern to establish along the transmission line. This is followed by an overview of twin-line and coaxial cable transmission line types, including their construction. Details are included within the chapter of how a transmission line can be made up to suit a particular application.

There is a chapter describing how different impedances can be matched using sections of transmission line, leading into the concept of common mode currents, their effect and how they can be minimised using balanced-to-unbalanced transitions (baluns) made using coaxial cable based techniques. There is a chapter summarising how coaxial cables can be fitted with connectors, including BNC, N and PL259 types. To enable an overview of the impedances that can be encountered along a transmission line, there is a chapter which introduces the use of the Smith Chart. There are three annexes that support material presented, where there was insufficient material to form a chapter in its own right.

1.2 Background Concepts

When a transmission line is energised with RF power, the current flowing in one conductor is equal but opposite to the current flowing in the other conductor. Both conductors will establish their own electromagnetic field, which are equal but opposite. As a result, both these fields will tend to cancel each other out, with any resultant field being negligible. Therefore, any electromagnetic radiation from the feeder cable will also be negligible, and so close to zero. This concept for a transmitter supplying RF power to the transmission line is illustrated in **Figure 1**.

Feeder cables tend to be of two types:

- Twin-line feeder cable

- Coaxial feeder cable

A twin-line feeder cable is constructed from two identical parallel conductors, which are kept at a fixed separation apart along the cable's length by the insulation between them. When carrying an RF signal, the uniform arrangement of the twin-line feeder cable maintains the equilibrium between the currents flowing within each conductor (and so also the electromagnetic fields). It is through maintaining this electrical equilibrium, between the conductors, why this type of transmission line is known as a balanced feeder cable.

It is possible to construct a twin-line feeder cable using two suitable single-core copper wires that are uniformly separated by polyethylene or plastic spac-

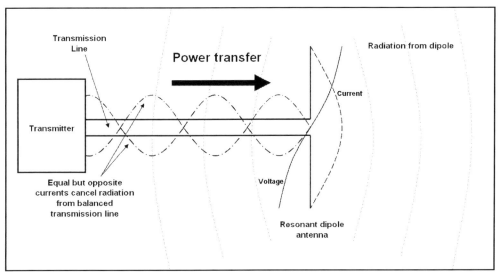

Figure 1: A transmission line conveying RF energy to an antenna. No radiation occurs from the line provided the RF energy on each of the conductors is equal and opposite. Once the RF energy reaches the antenna there is no opposition to radiation.

ers set at equal distances apart along the line's length. This arrangement is often referred to as an open-wire feeder. Commercially available twin-line feeder cables tend to come in two varieties. When the insulation runs continuously along their length, then this type of twin-line feeder is known as 'ribbon' cable. The other form of twin-line feeder has 'windows' set regularly at intervals within the insulation and this type of twin-line feeder is referred to as '*ladder-line*' or '*window-line*'. An example of a ladder-line feeder cable is shown in **Figure 2**. This type of cable is often used by amateur radio stations to provide the connection between the radio equipment and an HF antenna and has a nominal characteristic impedance of 300Ω.

A coaxial feeder cable is constructed from two conductors that are arranged concentrically. The inner conductor is supported by means of a semi-solid low-loss insulator between it and the outer surrounding conductor. When a coaxial feeder cable carries an RF signal, due to skin effect, the RF signal travels along the inner conductor's upper surface and the inside surface of the surrounding outer conductor. Under these circumstances, **the outer conductor's inner and outer surfaces can behave independently of each other**. It is for this reason why coaxial cables are known as unbalanced feeders. An example of the internal arrangement of the concentric con-

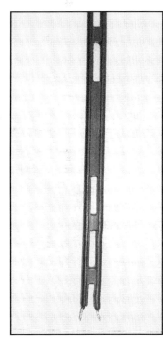

Figure 2: An example of a twin-line feeder cable is often used by amateur radio stations. This is type of feeder cable is often referred to as 'ladder-line'.

ductors for a typical coaxial feeder cable is shown in **Figure 3**. The coaxial cable illustrated is RG-213, with a characteristic impedance of 50Ω. This is an example of a coaxial cable often used by amateur radio stations to provide the connection between the radio equipment and the antenna.

Figure 3: An example of RG-213 coaxial feeder cable which is often used by amateur radio stations.

1.3 Main Abbreviations Used			
AC:	alternating current	Rg:	insulation's leakage resistance
B:	susceptance (in siemens, S)	RF:	radio frequency
Balun:	Balanced-to-unbalanced transition	SWG:	standard wire gauge
C:	capacitance (in farads, F)	SWR:	standing wave ratio
c:	speed of light or 300 000 000 m/s	V_{in}:	voltage applied at the input (in volts)
CMC:	common mode current(s)	V_{Load}:	voltage developed across a load (in volts)
dB:	decibel	V_{out}	voltage at the output (in volts)
f:	frequency (in hertz, Hz)	V_p	velocity of propagation
F:	capacitance in farads (unit)	W:	watts (measure of power)
G:	conductance (in siemens, S)	Y:	admittance (in siemens)
H:	inductance in henries (unit)	X:	reactance (in ohms, Ω)
Hz:	frequency in hertz (unit)	Z:	impedance (in ohms, Ω)
i:	current flowing (in amperes or amps, A)	Z_L:	the impedance of the load (in ohms, Ω)
k:	kilo (or x1000)	Zo:	characteristic impedance (in ohms, Ω)
L:	inductance (in Henries)	α:	attenuation coefficient
ℓ:	length	β:	phase-change coefficient of a transmission line
M:	mega (or x1,000,000)	γ:	propagation constant (in metres per second)
MHz:	megahertz	ε_r:	relative permittivity of a material
m:	milli (or 1×10^{-3} or x0.001)	λ:	wavelength
Pin:	power at the input (usually in watts)	μ:	micro (or 1×10^{-6} or x0.000 001)
Pout:	power at the output (usually in watts)	ρ:	reflection coefficient
p:	pico (or 1×10^{-12})	π:	3.141593
R:	resistance (in ohms, Ω)	Ω:	resistance in ohms (unit)

Primary and Secondary Line Coefficients

When considering how a transmission line functions, there are two sets of parameters that collectively, or individually, influence the line's performance. These are the primary and secondary line coefficients which are summarised as follows.

2.1 Primary Line Coefficients

A transmission line comprising a pair of parallel run conductors provides a connection between the near-end and far-end equipment. A voltage (V_{in}) applied across the input to the transmission line causes a current to flow (i) which energises the line as shown in **Figure 4**, where the end of the transmission line is terminated in a load. The physical and electrical properties of a conductive transmission line influence how the current (i) behaves, as it travels along the line. Consequently, this also has an effect on the current's relationship with the voltage developed across the line throughout its length.

Therefore, the physical and electrical properties of a transmission line determine its characteristics, which are described using four primary line coefficients of resistance, inductance, conductance and capacitance [1]. These coefficients can be considered as being uniformly distributed along, and blended throughout, the length of the line so that at no point is there any discontinuity between them in the form of a lumped component. These primary coefficients are summarised in the following.

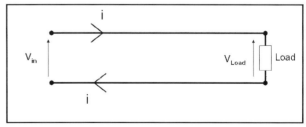

Figure 4: Concept of how the applied voltage V_{in} energises the line causing a current to flow along the line and through the terminating load.

Transmission Lines Explained

2.1.1 Loop Resistance

The transmission line's conductors are typically made from copper or aluminium and the voltage across the load (V_{Load}) is lower than V_{in}, so the line's loop resistance (R) is given by:

$$R(\Omega) = \frac{\left(V_{in} - V_{Load}\right)}{i}$$

The loop resistance is usually considered as being equally distributed between the transmission line's two conductors and this concept is shown in **Figure 5a** as R/2. The loop resistive coefficient (R) is measured in ohms (Ω) and is often quoted in ohms per 100m.

2.1.2 Loop Inductance

When an AC current is flowing in the transmission line's conductors, this causes an alternating magnetic field to be established around each conductor. When the magnetic field originated by one conductor 'strikes' the second conductor, then this induces a current into that conductor which opposes the main current flow. This effect also occurs with the second conductor, with its magnetic field also inducing an opposing current into the first conductor as well. This can be considered as a series inductive effect which is equally distributed between the two conductors forming the transmission line as shown in **Figure 5b** as L/2. The loop inductive (L) coefficient is measured in henries (H) and often quoted as henries per 100m.

2.1.3 Capacitance

The transmission line's two parallel conductors are separated by a distance (d), with this space filled by an insulator (eg plastic or air). Each conductor has a surface area (A) which runs uniformly along the length of the line. This scenario can be thought of as the plates of a capacitor which are separated by the insulation which has a dielectric constant (K). The line's capacitance (C) is then given by:

$$C(\text{farads}) = \frac{\left(k \times A\right)}{d}$$

This concept is represented by a parallel capacitor connected between the two conductors as is shown in **Figure 5c** as C. The capacitive coefficient (C) is measured in farads (F) and often quoted per 100m.

2.1.4 Conductance

The insulation between the two conductors cannot be perfect and so it allows a tiny current to flow between them; this is known as a leakage current. This

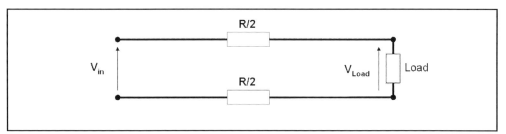

Figure 5a: A transmission line's distributed loop resistance (R) represented as two equal resistances (R/2) within the conductors forming the line.

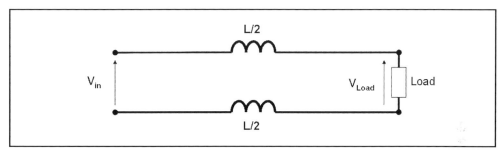

Figure 5b: A transmission line's distributed loop inductance (L) represented as two equal inductances (L/2) within the conductors forming the line.

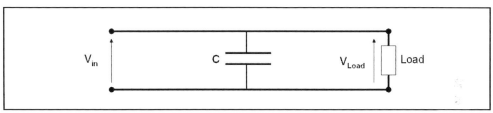

Figure 5c: A transmission line's parallel conductors can be considered as forming a capacitor (C) connected across the transmission line.

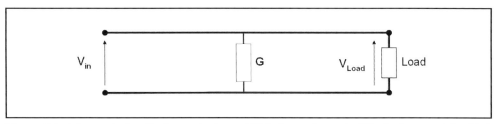

Figure 5d: A transmission line's conductance (G) is the reciprocal of the leakage resistor (Rg) connected across the transmission line. The leakage resistance (Rg) for a transmission line is usually extremely high and so this is why it is usually expressed a conductance (G) to ease with line calculations.

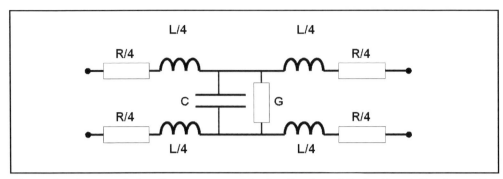

Figure 5e: A transmission line represented by its distributed R, L, C and G primary line coefficients.

current is very small because the insulation's resistance (Rg) is extremely high and is often many mega-ohms (MΩ) in value, making line calculations difficult to deal with. It is for this reason that the insulation's resistance is usually quoted as a conductance (G) to allow calculations to be more reasonable to handle. The insulation's conductance (G) is measured in siemens and is the reciprocal of the insulation's resistance (Rg), where:

$$G(S) = \frac{1}{\text{Leakage Resistance } (Rg)}$$

This concept is shown in **Figure 5d** as G. The leakage coefficient (G) is measured in siemens (S) and is often quoted per 100m.

2.1.5 Equivalent Circuit of a Transmission Line
Combining the coefficients R, L, C and G allows an equivalent circuit for a transmission line to be constructed as shown in **Figure 5e**, where R and L have been equally distributed along the line (as R/4 and L/4).

2.2 Secondary Line Coefficients
There are four secondary line coefficients [2] associated with transmission lines and these are the usual parameters which can be expected to be encountered when working with lines. These secondary coefficients are the characteristic impedance, the loss, the phase-lag and the velocity factor. These quantities can be determined directly from the primary line coefficients, however their detailed derivation has been avoided in the sections to follow.

2.2.1 The Characteristic Impedance of a Transmission Line (Zo).
If a transmission line could be made infinitely long, then if an RF voltage (V_{in}) is applied to the line's input it follows that this will cause an RF current (i) to flow (as shown conceptually in Figure 4). The characteristic impedance (Zo) of this

infinitely long transmission line is then given by:

$$Zo(\Omega) = \frac{V_{in}}{i}$$

If this line is cut somewhere along its length and terminated with an impedance equal to Zo, then transmission line will continue to behave as if it were still infinitely long.

Zo can also be found from taking the square root of the short-circuited impedance multiplied by the open-circuit impedance of the line, such that:

$$Zo(\Omega) = \sqrt{\left(Z_{short\text{-}circuit} \times Z_{open\text{-}circuit}\right)}$$

(1)

Referring to the concept of a transmission line as shown in Figure 5e, when the line is terminated in a short-circuit the input impedance has the loop resistance (R) and inductance (L) predominate. However, when the line is terminated in an open-circuit the input impedance has the capacitance (C) and conductance (G) predominate. Therefore, Figure 5e can be simplified to **Figures 6a and 6b** for the short-circuit and open-circuit impedance cases.

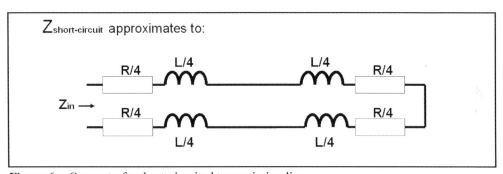

Figure 6a: Concept of a short-circuited transmission line.

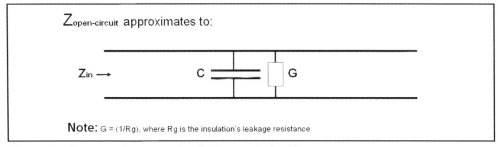

Figure 6b: Concept of an open-circuited transmission line.

Transmission Lines Explained

Referring to Figure 6a, where the transmission line effectively becomes a series connection of R and L, then:

$$Z_{\text{short-circuit}}\left(\Omega\right) = \left(R + j2 \cdot \pi \cdot f \cdot L\right)$$

where L becomes a reactance (X_L) because there is an RF current flowing through it, with this indicated by the use of j-notation.

Referring to Figure 6b, here the transmission line effectively becomes a parallel connection of C and the conductance G. To ease calculations, it is easier to express $Z_{\text{open-circuit}}$ as an admittance (Y) in siemens (S), where:

$$Z_{\text{open-circuit}}\left(\Omega\right) = \frac{1}{Y_{\text{open-circuit}}}$$

Here,

$$Y_{\text{open-circuit}}\left(S\right) = \left(G + j2 \cdot \pi \cdot f \cdot C\right)$$

In the equation above, G is the reciprocal of the insulation's leakage resistance (Rg), while C is expressed as a susceptance (B) which is the reciprocal of the capacitor's reactance (X_c). Using j-notation, X_c is expressed as:

$$X_c\left(\Omega\right) = \frac{-j}{\left(2 \cdot \pi \cdot f \cdot C\right)}$$

Hence, B is given by:

$$B\left(S\right) = \frac{1}{-jX_c} = +j2 \cdot \pi \cdot f \cdot C$$

Therefore:

$$Z_{\text{open-circuit}}\left(\Omega\right) = \frac{1}{\left(G + j2 \cdot \pi \cdot f \cdot C\right)}$$

where f is the frequency in hertz (Hz) in the equations above.

Returning to Equation 1 above, substituting $Z_{\text{short-circuit}}$ and $Z_{\text{open-circuit}}$ into Equation 1 gives Equation 2:

Characteristic impedance

$$Zo\ (\Omega) = \sqrt{\frac{(R + j2 \cdot \pi \cdot f \cdot L)}{(G + j2 \cdot \pi \cdot f \cdot C)}}$$

(2)

Equation 2 is one of the most fundamental equations when working with transmission lines and a number of other parameters can be determined from it.

However, at radio frequencies, the effects of R and G become very small compared to the reactive effects of L and C, allowing them to be ignored. As a result, this enables the "j.2. π.f" terms to be cancelled and Equation 2 simplifies to:

$$Zo(\Omega) \approx \sqrt{\frac{L}{C}}$$

(3)

From Equation 3, it can be seen that a transmission line's characteristic impedance (Zo) is resistive and is largely independent of the line's resistance, the line's conductance and the radio frequency used.

If the inductance and capacitance can be measured for a transmission line, then an indication of the line's characteristic impedance can be determined using Equation 3.

Example:
Typically, for some coaxial cables C is 100pF/m while L=0.25µH/m. Applying Equation 3, this gives a characteristic impedance of 50Ω.

Characteristic Impedance and Cable Dimensions
The characteristic impedance (Zo) of a transmission line can also be calculated if the physical dimensions of the conductors and the spacing between them are known.

Twin-Line Feeders
For a twin-line feeder cable, as shown in **Figure 7(a)**, Zo can be found using Equation 4:

$$Zo(\Omega) \approx \frac{276}{\sqrt{\varepsilon_r}} \cdot Log_{10}\left(\frac{D_s}{r}\right)$$

(4)

where D_s is the spacing between the centres of the two conductors and r is

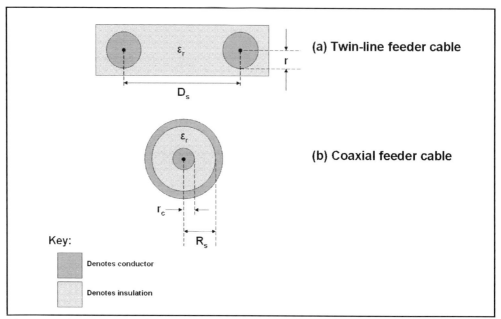

(a) Twin-line feeder cable

(b) Coaxial feeder cable

Key:

Denotes conductor

Denotes insulation

Figure 7: The parameters involved when calculating Zo for a twin-line cable (a) and coaxial cable (b).

the conductors' radius, both in millimetres (mm). ε_r is the relative permittivity of the continuous dielectric between the parallel conductors (insulation).

Example

For a twin conductor open-line feeder cable, if the radius of each conductor is 0.5mm and spacers hold the conductors 75mm apart, then using Equation 4 this gives Zo as close to 600Ω. For this line, the insulation between the conductors is air and this has ε_r close to 1.

Commercially available ladder-line twin feeder cable has regularly spaced windows cut into the polythene insulation between the conductors. This reduces the weight of the cable and gives an ε_r of close to 1 because the cable is mostly air spaced. The dimension of the conductors and the spacing between them gives a Zo of close to 300Ω for this type of cable. There is also a 450Ω version of this type of cable available which uses a wider spacing and is usually known as window-line.

Coaxial Feeders Cables

For a coaxial feeder cable as, shown in **Figure 7(b)**, Zo can be found using Equation 5:

$$Zo(\Omega) \approx \frac{138}{\sqrt{\varepsilon_r}} \cdot Log_{10}\left(\frac{R_s}{r_c}\right)$$

(5)

where R_s is the inside radius of the outer conductor and r_c is the radius of the inner conductor in millimetres (mm). ε_r is the relative permittivity of the of the continuous dielectric between the concentric conductors (insulation). For air ε_r is very close to 1 and for polythene ε_r is about 2.3. Typical insulators used for coaxial feeder cable include polythene, polystyrene and PTFE. However, some cables use air as the insulation with regularly spaced plastic discs used to maintain the separation between the outer and inner conductors. This arrangement of the cable gives ε_r close to 1.

The cable's inner round conductor can be made either from a single solid conductor, or from several strands which are regularly twisted axially along the length to give a conductor of the appropriate diameter. Some cables have a solid outer conductor, while others have an outer conductor which is composed of closely braided strands which allow these cables to be more flexible. Often a braid outer conductor is run over a conductive foil which encases the insulation between the inner and outer conductors. This foil helps any undesirable signal leakage or radiation from the cable to be reduced, so improving the cable's losses at higher frequencies.

2.2.2 Transmission Line Loss

The level of an RF signal applied to a transmission line will become progressively reduced, or attenuated, as the signal travels down the line. This reduction in the RF signal is primarily due to the loop resistance (R) of the conductors and, to some extent, by the parallel resistance (Rg) of the insulation between the conductors. For line calculations, Rg is usually expressed as a conductance (G) and is the reciprocal of Rg (ie G = 1/Rg), with this convention being used in the text to follow.

Starting with Figure 5e for reference, a transmission line can be presented as a sequence of equivalent circuits which are connected in series. Within the operating frequency range of the transmission line, the loop inductance (L) and parallel capacitance (C) components tend to have a lesser effect on the signal's attenuation when compared to the loop resistance (R) and the insulation's conductance (G). Therefore, it is possible to represent the transmission line using only the R and G components and this concept is shown in **Figure 8.** An RF voltage (V_{in})

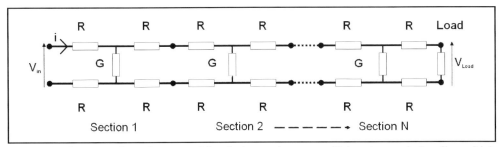

Figure 8: Concept of conductor and insulation resistances within a transmission line which attenuate a signal applied to the line.

applied to the input of the transmission line causes a current (i) to flow into the line. Both the voltage and current amplitudes are exponentially reduced as the RF signal travels down the line encountering the R and G components on route. At a point (ℓ) along the line the voltage (V_ℓ) and current (i_ℓ) can be found from:

$$V_\ell = V_{in} \cdot e^{-\alpha\ell}$$

(6a)

$$i_\ell = i_{in} \cdot e^{-\alpha\ell}$$

(6b)

where ℓ is the distance in metres down the line down the line from the line's input. The term e is the base for natural logarithms (2.7183). The term α is called the attenuation coefficient and is in nepers per metre.

Figure 9 illustrates an example of how the current (i_ℓ) exponentially decays along a transmission line as its length (ℓ) increases using Equation 6b above. The curve in Figure 9 could have also been plotted using the voltage (V_ℓ) applied to the input of the transmission line, which decays in the same manner.

It should be noted that Equations 6a and 6b do not take into account any RF signal loss through radiation from the transmission line itself. Radiation loss can occur in twin-line feeder cables when the separation between the conductors becomes an appreciable fraction of the RF signal's wavelength. However, for coaxial cables, radiation loss tends to be negligible due to the screening properties of the outer conductor, although some radiation loss can occur with braided outer conductors. (There is also a type of coaxial cable called 'leaky feeder' that has slots in the shielding, which gives controlled radiation along its length. It is often used in tunnels to provide radio coverage where signals would not normally propagate.)

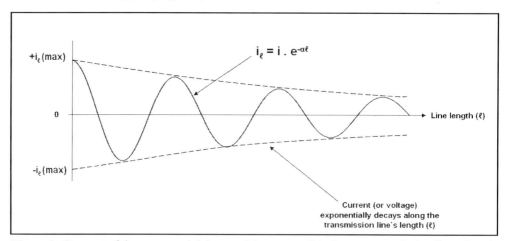

Figure 9: Concept of the exponential decay of the current (i_ℓ) along a transmission line's length (ℓ) as it travels down the line. The voltage (V_ℓ) applied to the transmission line also decays in the same manner.

Transmission Line Loss Measurement

A practical method to determine the loss of a transmission line is to measure the RF power (P_{in}) supplied to the input of the line and then to measure the RF power delivered at the output of the line (P_{out}). The transmission line's loss can then be calculated from the ratio of the power readings using Equation 7:

$$Loss(dB) = 10 \cdot Log_{10} \left(\frac{P_{in}}{P_{out}} \right)$$

(7)

The usual method to make these measurements is to use a power meter that is referred to the characteristic impedance of the transmission line (Zo). The transmit RF power supplied to the transmission line must be maintained at a constant level during the measurement of P_{in} and P_{out}.

When Zo is resistive, the power (P) is given by:

$$Power(P) = \frac{(voltage)^2}{Zo} \text{ in watts(W)}$$

By substituting this expression into Equation 7, the transmission line's loss can then be determined by measuring the RF voltages at the input (V_{in}) and output (V_{out}) of the line using Equation 8, when the line is terminated in a dummy load whose impedance equals Zo:

$$Loss (dB) = 20 \cdot Log_{10} \left(\frac{V_{in}}{V_{out}} \right)$$

(8)

The two RF voltage measurements are made using a suitable RF voltmeter capable of accurately working at the frequency used. Similarly, the transmit RF power supplied to the transmission line must be maintained at a constant level during the measurements. To make these measurements, physical access is needed to the transmission line's conductors at the near- and far-ends, however this is not always practical.

Loss and Frequency

At radio frequencies, the loop resistance loss is a function of skin-effect because this determines the effective area of the conductor carrying the RF current. Skin-effect [3] is given by:

$$Skin\ depth\ (mm) = \frac{66.2}{\sqrt{f}}$$

where f is the frequency in Hz.

As the frequency is increased, so the skin-effect's depth becomes shallower and the loop resistance becomes higher (with all other conditions remaining the same). Therefore, the transmission line's loss will theoretically increase according to the square root of the frequency. Consequently, it is possible to gain an indication of the loss presented by a transmission line at a higher frequency (f_{High}) compared to a lower frequency (f_{Low}) using Equation 9:

$$\text{Loss at } f_{High} \approx \left(\text{Loss at } f_{Low}\right) \cdot \sqrt{\frac{f_{High}}{f_{Low}}}$$

$$(9)$$

where the loss, in this case, is taken as the actual power ratio rather than in dB. However, for higher values of f_{High} Equation 9 becomes more inaccurate. When f_{High} is about three to four times higher than f_{Low}, then using Equation 9 is not recommended.

2.2.3 Phase-Change Coefficient in Transmission Lines

As an RF signal travels down a transmission line, it experiences a progressive phase lag (or difference) compared to its phase at the transmission line's input. The phase-change coefficient (β) of a transmission line is the number of degrees, or radians, phase lag per metre.

Note: 2.π radians (approximately 6.2832) equals 360°.

As the RF signal travels down the line, at a distance of one wavelength (λ) a phase lag of 360° or 2.π radians occurs, so:

$$\lambda \text{ (metres)} = \frac{2 \cdot \pi}{\beta}$$

$$(10)$$

where β is in radians.

Figure 10 illustrates an example of how the RF voltage applied to the line's input exponentially decays along a transmission line as its length increases due to the effect of the line's attenuation coefficient (α). The horizontal scale is shown in degrees as the voltage (shown as a wave) goes through each cycle, although radians could have been used. The wave is shown at the instant when the maximum RF voltage is applied to the line's input (10V in this case) and this represents the time "now", with the wave shown decaying as time has elapsed. The phase lags A, B and C are shown where the wave is at its peak and then fallen to zero, although any part of the wave's structure could have been chosen. The time differences between phase lags A, B and C are equal and illustrate that the phase-change coefficient (β) has not changed (ie the frequency of the wave applied remains constant).

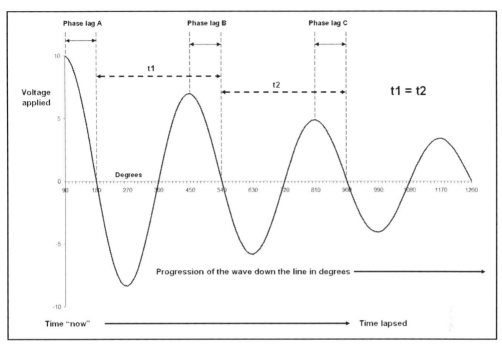

Figure 10: As an RF signal travels down a transmission line, it experiences a phase lag (β), however the time differences between phase lags A, B and C are equal.

Example

When $\beta = 2°$ per metre, then at 10 meters along the line the RF signal experiences a phase lag of 20° (or 0.349 radians).

2.2.4 Velocity of Propagation, Velocity Factor and Transmission Lines

When travelling in free space, an RF electromagnetic wave travels at the velocity of the speed of light (c). However, when an RF electromagnetic wave is applied as an RF signal to the input of a transmission line, then the RF signal travels, or propagates, at a much slower velocity than the speed of light down the line. The velocity at which the RF signal travels down the line is known as the velocity of propagation (V_p) and is a function of the RF signal's wavelength (λ) and frequency (f), where:

$$V_p \,(\text{metres/second}) = \lambda \cdot f \tag{11}$$

Using Figure 5e again for reference, a transmission line can be presented as a sequence of equivalent circuits which are connected in series. Within the operating frequency range of the transmission line, the insulation's parallel resistive component (G) and loop resistive component (R) tend to have a lesser effect on the RF signal's propagation along the line compared to the loop inductive (L) and parallel capacitance (C) components. Therefore, it is possible to represent

Transmission Lines Explained

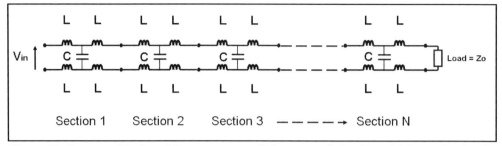

Figure 11: Concept of the L and C components within a transmission line which retard a signal's velocity along the line.

the transmission line using only the L and C components and this concept is shown in **Figure 11**. Essentially, the transmission line now behaves as if it was a low-pass filter and, at radio frequencies, the phase-change coefficient is now given by Equation 12:

$$\beta \ (\text{radians/metre}) \ = 2 \cdot \pi \cdot f \cdot \sqrt{L \cdot C} \tag{12}$$

In the distance of one wavelength (λ), a phase-lag (β) of $2.\pi$ radians occurs as previously described by Equation 10:

$$\lambda = \frac{2 \cdot \pi}{\beta}$$

The velocity of propagation (V_p) can then be determined from the L and C of the transmission line from Equation 13, where:

$$V_p \ = \lambda \cdot f \ = \left(\frac{2 \times \pi}{\beta}\right) \cdot f \ = \ \frac{2 \cdot \pi \cdot f}{2 \cdot \pi \cdot f \cdot \sqrt{L \cdot C}} \ = \ \frac{1}{\sqrt{L \cdot C}} \tag{13}$$

where V_p is in metres/second.

The effect of Vp on an RF signal propagating down the transmission is to shorten its wavelength (λ) because the RF signal is travelling slower than the speed of light while the frequency (f) remains the same (Equation 11). V_p is often quoted as a fraction compared to the speed of light (c) and this is often given as a velocity factor, which is typically 0.6c to 0.9c, though in practice the letter c is often omitted.

Example
Typically for some coaxial cables C is 100pF/m while L=0.25µH/m. Applying Equation 13 gives a velocity of propagation for the RF signal along the line of

18

200 million meters/second, or 0.666c. Thus its velocity factor would usually be stated as 0.66 (or, more accurately, 0.67).

2.3 The Propagation Constant
As described previously, using Equation 2, the characteristic impedance (Zo) of a transmission line can be calculated from the line's primary coefficients of:

Loop resistance   (R)
Loop inductance   (L)
Conductance   (G)
Capacitance   (C)

with these coefficients often quoted on a per 100m basis.

$$Zo(\Omega) = \sqrt{\frac{(R + j2 \cdot \pi \cdot f \cdot L)}{(G + j2 \cdot \pi \cdot f \cdot C)}}$$

(2)

R, L, G and C also allow the propagation constant (γ) [4] for the wave travelling down the transmission line to be calculated, where:

$$(\gamma) = \sqrt{(R + j2 \times \pi \times f \times L) \times (G + j2 \times \pi \times f \times C)}$$

(14)

where γ is usually quoted on a per metre basis.

The propagation constant (γ) describes the logarithmic rate of decay of a signal waveform in terms of how it has travelled down a transmission line. Therefore, the propagation constant (γ) relates to both the transmission line's loss and to the phase-change of a wave travelling down the line. Consequently, the propagation constant (γ) comprises a real term and an imaginary term (denoted by j). The real term gives the attenuation coefficient (α), while the imaginary term gives the phase-change coefficient (β). Hence there is a relationship between γ, α and β such that:

$$(\gamma) = \alpha + j\beta$$

where the attenuation coefficient (α) is in nepers per metre and the phase-change coefficient (β) is the number of degrees, or radians, phase lag per metre.

Note:
Sometimes the propagation constant (γ) may be called the loss coefficient.

Further information relating to the propagation constant (γ) for a transmission line has been included as Annex 1, along with two examples for completeness.

Transmission Lines Explained

Travelling Waves, Reflected Waves and Standing Waves

3.1 Travelling Waves

When the phase change coefficient (β) was described previously, the concept was introduced of an RF signal travelling as a wave down a transmission line at a specific velocity of propagation (V_p). This concept is illustrated in **Figure 12** where the transmitter is represented by a generator that rotates a voltage

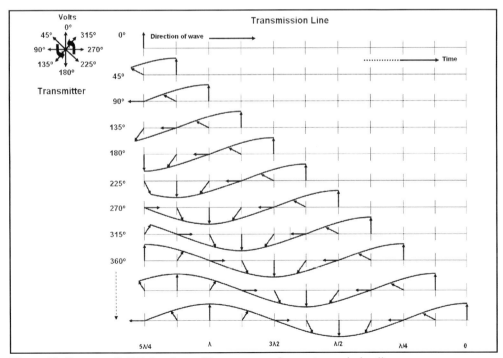

Figure 12: Concept of a RF signal travelling as a wave down a transmission line,

vector anti-clockwise starting at 0° and moving around to 360°, taking time to make a full cycle.

The generator's voltage vector rotates at a constant rate and so applies, in this case, a sinusoidal voltage to the transmission line's input. If the voltage level applied to the line is plotted against the vector's angle, as time passes, the signal travelling down the line takes the form of a sine wave. As successive regular cycles of the generator are completed, the waveform repeats itself at a constant frequency (f) and there is a distinct distance between the successive peaks (or troughs) of the travelling wave. This distinct distance between peaks (or troughs) is referred to as the wavelength (λ). Therefore, the travelling wave propagates down the line at a velocity as described previously by Equation 11:

$$\text{Vp (meters/second)} = \lambda \cdot f$$

(11)

As the transmitter generates a voltage, and this is applied to the transmission line, this causes a current to flow in the line. This current is in phase with the voltage because the characteristic impedance Zo of the transmission line is resistive (as described previously). Therefore, power is supplied by the transmitter to the line and this travels as a wave down the line to be absorbed by the load connected to the end of the line.

3.2 Mismatch and Standing Waves

Figure 12 illustrated the concept of an RF signal propagating as a travelling wave down a transmission line from the transmitter towards the load [5]. This transmitted RF signal is referred to as the *incident wave*. The transmission line in Figure 12 is represented by a single horizontal line to help simplify the diagram and this technique is also used in the subsequent diagrams which follow.

When the transmission line, with a characteristic impedance Zo, is terminated by a load (eg an antenna) whose impedance is different to Zo, then there is said to be a *mismatch* between the load and the transmission line. A transmitter connected to the transmission line's input applies an RF signal to the line. This RF signal travels down the line as the incident wave towards the load terminating the transmission line. When the incident wave encounters a load with an impedance that is not the same as Zo, then not all the power is absorbed and some of the incident wave's energy is reflected back towards the transmitter. This RF signal returned by the load is referred to as the *reflected wave*. Only when the load's impedance and the transmission line's impedance are equal will the maximum power be transferred to the load. This condition is referred to as being *matched* and relates to the maximum power transfer theorem as described in Annex 2.

Note:
If a transmission line is damaged somewhere along its length, then this can affect the line's characteristic impedance (Zo) and this is known as a *discontinuity*. A discontinuity behaves in a similar way as a load mismatch and can establish a reflected wave.

The Voltage Standing Wave
The concept of the incident and reflected waves is shown in **Figure 13** as voltage vectors. The solid vector represents the incident wave while the dotted vector represents the reflected wave returned by the load towards the transmitter. In this case, the load in Figure 13 is a short-circuit and the entire incident wave is returned as the reflected wave (it is as if the far-end of the line now has its own generator applying the reflected wave back up the line). The incident and reflected waves algebraically combine as shown in Figure 13 and the resultant is a static interference pattern known as a standing wave. This is depicted in Figure 13 as the lower diagram where the magnitude of the voltage standing wave is shown. The standing wave repeats at regular intervals and each peak (or trough) is separated by a distance of a half wavelength ($\lambda/2$). The load in Figure 13 is a short-circuit, therefore the voltage has to be zero and this is represented by the incident and reflected voltage vectors at the load being equal

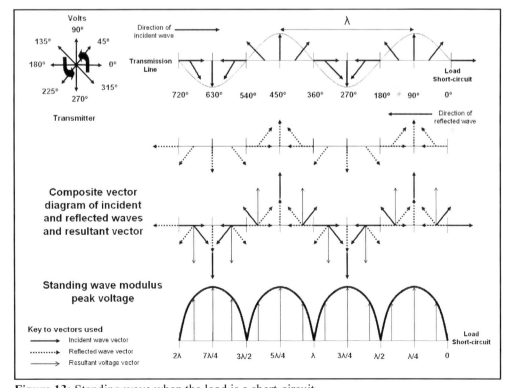

Figure 13: Standing wave when the load is a short-circuit.

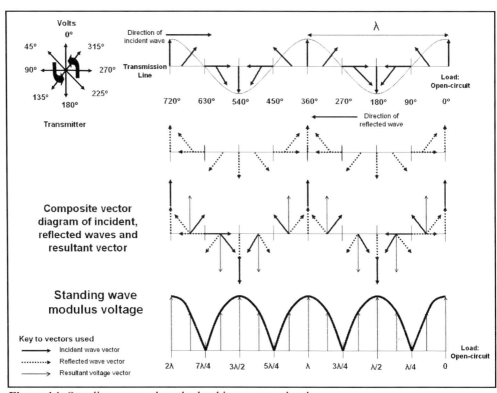

Figure 14: Standing wave when the load is an open-circuit.

but opposite. However, at a quarter wavelength (λ/4) down the line the vectors are now additive and the standing wave's peak voltage is double the incident wave's voltage. This pattern continues to be repeated at multiples of λ/2 down the line.

The concept when the load is an open-circuit is shown in **Figure 14** for the incident and reflected waves as vectors. Similarly, the solid vector represents the incident wave while the dotted vector represents the reflected wave reflected by the load back up the line. Again, the entire incident wave is returned as the reflected wave. Both the waves algebraically combine as shown in Figure 14 to form a standing wave. This is depicted in Figure 14 as the lower diagram where the magnitude of the voltage standing wave is shown. Similarly, the standing wave repeats at regular intervals and each peak (or trough) is separated by a distance of a half wavelength (λ/2). However, compared to the short-circuit load situation described in Figure 13, the standing wave pattern is shifted by a quarter wavelength (λ/4) as shown. The load in Figure 14 is an open-circuit, therefore the incident and reflected vectors are now additive and the voltage across the load (ie across the line's open end) is now twice that of the incident wave as shown. This situation repeats every λ/2 back down the line with the standing wave's peak voltage being double the incident wave's voltage.

The Current Standing Wave:

There is a similar situation happening with the current vectors, however for the short-circuit load situation described in Figure 13 the incident and reflected current vectors are additive and the current flowing in the short-circuit load is now twice that of the incident current wave. The standing wave pattern for the current then takes on the form as shown in Figure 14. Similarly, when the load is an open-circuit as shown in Figure 14, the current has to be zero. This is represented by the incident and reflected current vectors at the load being equal but opposite. The current standing wave pattern then takes on the form as shown in Figure 13.

The short and open-circuit cases used in the above explanations represent the extreme cases and may only occur under fault conditions for example. Typically, the load's impedance will be somewhere between these two conditions and so affects the magnitude of the standing wave.

3.3 Reflection Coefficient and Standing Wave Ratio

The ratio of the reflected to incident wave amplitudes is called the reflection coefficient, designated by the Greek letter ρ (Rho). If the reflected power travelling down the line and the incident power travelling up the line can be measured, then the reflection coefficient (ρ) can be calculated from:

$$\rho = \sqrt{\frac{\text{Reflected power in watts}}{\text{Incident power in watts}}}$$

Similarly, if the reflected volts and the incident volts across the line can be measured, then the reflection coefficient (ρ) can also be calculated from:

$$\rho = \frac{\text{Reflected volts}}{\text{Incident volts}}$$

The value of ρ can be calculated using Equation 15:

$$|\rho| = \left|\frac{Z_L - Z_O}{Z_L + Z_O}\right| \tag{15}$$

where Z_L is the load impedance and Zo is the characteristic impedance of the transmission line. The vertical lines either side of the quantities shown in Equation 15 show that the modulus values are used in the calculation (ie not complex values). It follows that the magnitude of ρ lies between 0 and 1. When ρ is 0, this indicates the condition for a perfectly matched line.

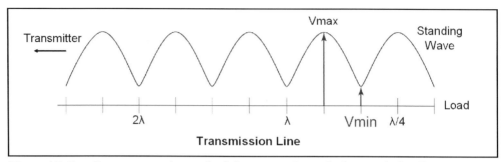

Figure 15: Standing wave maxima and minima on a mismatched transmission line.

Figure 15 illustrates the standing wave pattern established along a transmission line when the load impedance (Z_L) is not an open or short-circuit, but is somewhere in between. Figure 15 shows the voltage standing wave has a maximum value (V_{max}) and minimum value (V_{min}). The standing wave ratio (SWR) is defined as the ratio of the voltage maximum to the voltage minimum along a transmission line and can be determined from Equation 16:

$$SWR = \frac{V_{max}}{V_{min}}$$
(16)

Sometimes, Equation 16 may be referred to as the voltage standing wave ratio (VSWR).

Similarly, there will be current maxima and minima along the transmission line. The SWR can also be defined as the ratio of the maximum to the minimum current along a transmission line and can be determined from Equation 17:

$$SWR = \frac{I_{max}}{I_{min}}$$
(17)

SWR can be measured using either a current or voltage sensor. The maximum must always be greater than the minimum, therefore SWR is always greater than or equal to one. If no reflections exist, then no standing wave pattern exists along the line and the voltage or current values measured at all points along the transmission line are equal (disregarding the effect of loss). In this case the impedance match is said to be perfect, the numerator and denominator of Equations 16 and 17 are equal, and SWR equals unity. As can be seen from Figure 15 the direct measurement of SWR must be made at two positions along the line which are a quarter-wavelength ($\lambda/4$) apart. However, by using the reflectometer the SWR can be measured indirectly using Equation 18:

$$SWR = \frac{1 + |\rho|}{1 - |\rho|}$$

(18)

Substituting Equation 15 as ρ into the above and rearranging the equation gives:

$$SWR = \frac{Z_L}{Zo} \text{ when } Z_L \text{ is larger than } Zo$$

(19a)

or

$$SWR = \frac{Zo}{Z_L} \text{ when } Zo \text{ is larger than } Z_L$$

(19b)

It is often thought that a high SWR causes the transmission line to radiate. This is not true, provided the power on each line is equal and opposite (as previously shown in Figure 1).

3.4 SWR Measurement

The reflectometer is an instrument used for measuring ρ and comprises two power meters, one reading incident power and the other reflected power. Power detector directivity is possible because the incident voltage and current waves are in phase, while in the reflected waves they are 180° out of phase.

The reflectometer, calibrated in SWR, has become the standard amateur radio tool for measuring transmission line mismatch. Many commercially available Antenna Tuning Units (ATU) incorporate an integral reflectometer whose output is displayed on an SWR meter using two indicator needles. One needle shows forward power, while the other shows the reflected power. The SWR is read where the two needles cross and **Figure 16** illustrates a typical SWR meter display, in this case indicating a SWR of approximately 1.4:1.

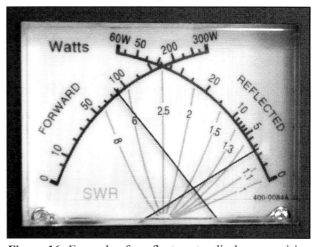

Figure 16: Example of a reflectometer display comprising two power meters within the same unit, one reading incident power and the other reflected power.

3.5 Losses due to SWR

As previously described, a transmission line has losses due to the loop resistance (R) of its conductors and the insulation between them (G) as illustrated in Figure 8. Losses at higher frequencies can also result from the conductive quality of the conductor's outer surface from skin-effect [3]. For this reason, some transmission lines have the outer surface of their copper conductors silver plated to help reduce skin-effect losses (silver is a better electrical conductor than copper). **Figure 17** shows approximate losses for 450Ω twin-line cable and RG-213 coaxial cable when they are terminated with a load equal to each cable's characteristic impedance (Zo).

Additional losses are also introduced due to load/transmission line mismatches (SWR) as shown in Figure 17 for 450Ω twin-line cable and RG-213 coaxial cable (where the load could be an antenna for example). The losses shown in Figure 17 are for a transmission line over 10m long and it can be seen that SWR losses on the HF bands are not as great as is often may be thought, although at VHF and UHF it is a different matter. As can be seen from Figure 17, even when the SWR is 5:1 on a 30m length of RG-213 coaxial cable at 28MHz, then the attenuation is only just over 1dB higher compared to the perfectly terminated loss case.

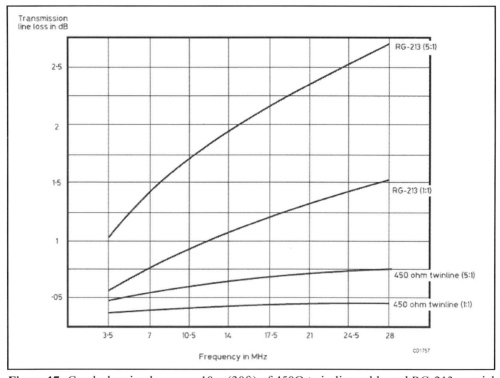

Figure 17: Graph showing losses on 10m (30ft) of 450Ω twin-line cable and RG-213 coaxial cable at an SWR of 1:1 and 5:1.

3.5.1 The masking effect of attenuation

When there is a mismatch between the transmission line and its terminating load (eg an antenna), not all the incident RF power is absorbed by the load. The proportion of RF power which is not absorbed is reflected back down the transmission line as reflected RF power. The transmission line's losses attenuate the reflected RF power and so tend to mask the mismatch at the transmitting end, so reducing the SWR reading at the transmitter. This can give an inaccurate indication of the actual mismatch between the transmission line and its terminating load.

To investigate the impact on the apparent match between a load (eg an antenna) and the transmission line, the following analysis uses attenuation to represent the transmission line for ease of explanation. The standing wave produced as a result of a mismatch will also have an influence, however the situation described provides a reasonable insight into how the degree of mismatch can be masked by the transmission line's loss. The scenarios provided can be thought of as representative when the operating wavelength (λ) is long compared to a lossy transmission line's length.

The effect of 3dB of attenuation:
Figure 18(A) illustrates a theoretical attenuator giving a loss of 3dB between Point A and B. This attenuator has been calculated to give the values of resistors R1, R2 and R3 shown assuming a resistive load and a Zo of 50Ω.

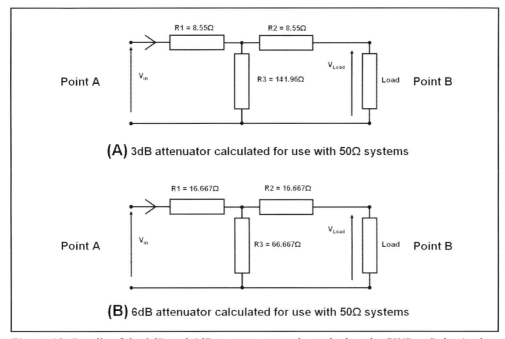

(A) 3dB attenuator calculated for use with 50Ω systems

(B) 6dB attenuator calculated for use with 50Ω systems

Figure 18: Details of the 3dB and 6dB attenuators used to calculate the SWR at Point A when the load's impedance varies at Point B.

For the 3dB attenuation, the SWR calculated at Point A is higher than that calculated for the 6dB attenuation. Effectively, the mismatch at Point B has been masked by both the attenuators, with the perceived match at Point A apparently improving as the attenuation is increased.

At Point A, the impact of the masking effect of both attenuators becomes significant as the mismatch at Point B becomes extreme. Therefore, when using an SWR meter to measure the SWR at the radio equipment's end of the transmission line, this can lead to a false impression of the actual degree of mismatch between the antenna and the transmission line at Point B because the SWR appears low. This has the consequence of the power actually radiated by the antenna being lower than it should be. In addition, the masking effect may make the receiver appear less sensitive than it actually is because some of received signal is lost as a result of the mismatch between the antenna and the transmission line.

3.6 Loss Measurement using SWR Measurements

The difference in the SWR readings between the transmitter and antenna (load) ends of the transmission line, due to a mismatch, mean it is possible to use an SWR meter to measure the transmission line's loss. As described previously, a reading of SWR at the transmitter's end of the transmission line, due to a mismatched load, will be lower than when the measurement is taken at the load's end (eg the antenna). The reason for this is that the transmission line's loss attenuates the reflected wave and tends to mask the mismatch at the transmitting end, so reducing the SWR reading at the transmitter.

To take this measurement, the transmission line is terminated with a load which creates a mismatch (eg 100Ω when the transmission line's Zo is 50Ω). Using a suitable SWR meter, the SWR is measured at the transmitter's end followed by measuring the SWR at the antenna's end. Using the two SWR readings obtained, an indication of the transmission line's loss can be found using the alignment chart in **Figure 20** [6].

Example
If the SWR measured at the transmitter's end of the transmission line is 1.2:1 and at the antenna's end is 1.45:1, then using Figure 20 the transmission line's loss is close to 3dB.

3.7 Effect of SWR on the Transmitter

As described above, the effect of a mismatch is to establish a pattern of voltage or current peaks at regular intervals of λ/2 along the transmission line. If the output stage of the transmitter happens to located at, or close to, a voltage or current peak then this could result in the possibility of the output stage being damaged. Many commercially available transceivers have the facility to moni-

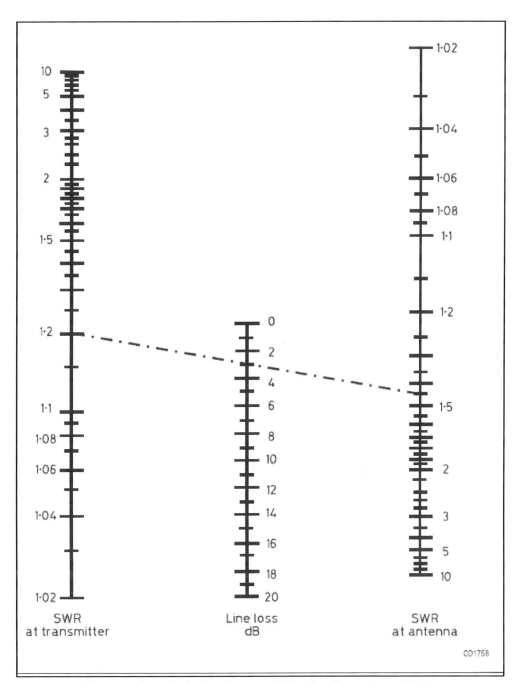

Figure 20: Alignment chart for finding the transmission line loss using an SWR meter.

tor the SWR and have a protection mechanism which automatically reduces the transmitter's RF power level if a specific SWR threshold is exceeded, eg a SWR of 2:1.

3.8 Factors to Consider when Choosing Coaxial Cables

The approximate attenuation figures for various correctly terminated coaxial cables are shown in **Figure 21**. These attenuation figures are for cable lengths of 30m and indicate that for frequencies below 30MHz there is not much to be gained by using low-loss coaxial feeders. However, at VHF and particularly UHF frequencies, it is a different matter because low-loss coaxial cable can really enhance a station's performance. For a typical UHF installation, about a 3dB improvement should be possible by replacing RG-213 with, for example, LDF4-50. This improvement may not sound very much, however the size of a VHF/UHF antenna array generally has to be doubled to obtain a 3dB improvement in gain.

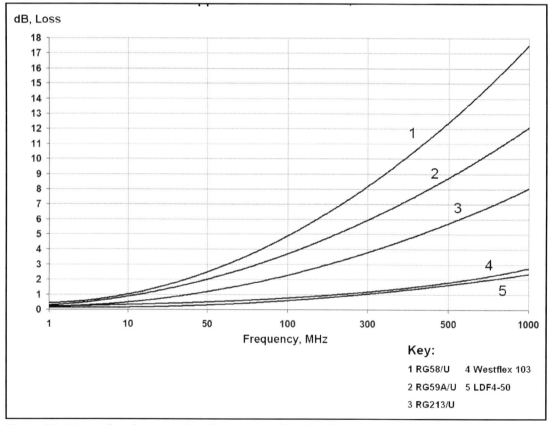

Figure 21: Attenuation characteristics of various 30m lengths of correctly terminated coaxial cables. With the exception of the thin RG58 coax the attenuation differences of the various cables below 30MHz are not significant.

Twin-Line and Coaxial Transmisison Lines

There are basically two forms of transmission line cable which could be selected to interconnect the antenna with the radio equipment within a radio station. These are the twin-line and coaxial feeder cable types, each of which has a different form of construction. However, both these cable types comprise two conductors run in close proximity. There is a third type of feeder which is often used at microwave frequencies, this taking the form of usually a rectangular profile metal tube known as a waveguide. However, in the sections to follow only twin-line and coaxial feeder cables have been considered.

When a transmission line is energised with RF power, the RF current flowing in one conductor is equal but opposite to the RF current flowing in the other conductor. Both conductors will establish their own electro-magnetic field. However, these fields will be equal but opposite and so tend to cancel each other out, with any resultant field being negligible. Therefore, any electromagnetic radiation from the feeder cable will also be negligible and so close to zero.

4.1 Twin-Line Feeder Cable

A twin-line feeder cable is constructed from two identical parallel conductors which are kept at a fixed separation by the insulation (or dielectric) between them along the cable's length. When carrying an RF signal, the equilibrium between the RF currents flowing within each conductor is maintained by the uniform physical structure of the twin-line feeder cable. Accordingly, the magnetic fields, generated by the RF currents, which surround the conductors are maintained equal but opposite, resulting in minimal radiation by the transmission line.

It is through maintaining this electrical equilibrium between the conductors why twin-line cables are known as balanced feeders. It is possible to construct an open-wire twin-line feeder cable using two suitable single core wires which are uniformly separated using plexiglass, polyethylene or plastic spacers set at

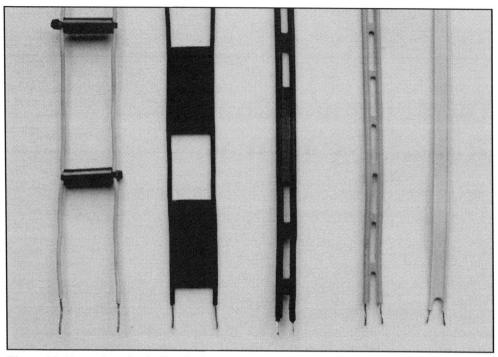

Figure 22: Examples of twin-line feeder cables. From left to right: 460Ω twin-line constructed using SWG18 insulated wire, plastic spacers and cable-ties. 450Ω 'window' twin-line. Two examples of 300Ω ladder-line. 300Ω ribbon cable.

equal distances apart along the line's length. Commercially available twin-line feeder cables tend to come in two varieties. When the insulation runs continuously along the twin-line cable's length, then this type of cable is known as 'ribbon' cable. The other form of twin-line feeder has 'windows' set at regular intervals within the insulation and this type of twin-line feeder is referred to as 'ladder-line' or 'window-line'. The introduction of 'windows' reduces the weight of the line, lowers the loss due to the dielectric being primarily air and breaks up the surface area where dirt and moisture could accumulate. Some examples of twin-line feeder cables have been shown in **Figure 22**.

4.1.1 Making Up a Twin-Line Feeder Cable

The concept of a twin-line feeder cable was previously shown in Figure 7(a) and its characteristic impedance (Zo) can be found using Equation 4:

$$Zo(\Omega) \approx \frac{276}{\sqrt{\varepsilon_r}} \cdot Log_{10}\left(\frac{D_s}{r}\right)$$

$$(4)$$

where D_s is the spacing between the centres of the two conductors, r is the conductors' radius (both in mm) and ε_r is the relative permittivity of the insulation between the parallel conductors.

If the insulation is primarily air, then ε_r is very close to 1. When using a conductor of 18 SWG, this has a radius (r) of 0.625mm. Then, with a spacing (D_s) of 7.5mm between two of these conductors, this gives:

$$Zo \approx 276 \times Log_{10}\left(\frac{7.5}{0.625}\right) = 298\Omega$$

This arrangement gives an impedance very close to commercially available 300Ω air-spaced twin-line (usually termed ladder-line).

Using the same conductor diameter and keeping air as the insulation, then a spacing (D_s) of 25mm gives:

$$Zo \approx 276 \times Log_{10}\left(\frac{25}{0.625}\right) = 442\Omega$$

Figure 23a. Example of a twin-line feeder cable constructed using insulated 18SWG wire, 25mm long spacers and cable ties. This arrangement gave a measured characteristic impedance of close to 460Ω.

This arrangement gives an impedance very close to commercially available 450Ω air-spaced twin-line (usually termed 'window-line').

Twin-line feeder construction example

An 8m long twin-line feeder cable is described, which was used to feed a doublet antenna. The twin-line feeder cable was made up using 18 SWG plastic insulated single core copper conductor, plastic spacers of diameter 8mm by 25mm long (each with a hole able to take an M4 sized bolt through the centre) and cable ties. The spacers were situated approximately 75mm apart along the line between the conductors. Each spacer was held in place using a cable tie passed through the spacer, around a conductor, then doubled-back on itself through the spacer, round the second conductor and then tightened up. **Figure 23a** shows the construction used, with **Figure 23b** showing a close-up of one spacer's assembly.

The insulation between the two conductors was primarily air, giving ε_r very close to 1. The 18 SWG conductor used had a radius (r) of 0.625mm and was covered with a plastic outer of 1mm in thickness. Using Equation 4 and allowing for each conductor's insulation thickness, the spacing (Ds) was close to 27mm, giving:

Figure 23b: Closer view of the twin-line feeder cable's construction.

$$Zo \approx 276 \times Log_{10}\left(\frac{27}{0.625}\right) = 451\Omega$$

To obtain an indication of the twin-line feeder cable's characteristic imped-ance (Zo), measurements were made using an MFJ 269c antenna analyser of the cable's open-circuit and short-circuit impedances from 2 to 6MHz (using steps of 0.5MHz). Using these measurements, this enabled the characteristic impedance (Zo) to be calculated by using Equation 1:

$$Zo(\Omega) = \sqrt{\left(Z_{short\text{-}circuit} \times Z_{open\text{-}circuit}\right)}$$

(1)

Figure 24 plots the results obtained from the measurements, indicating that the characteristic impedance (Zo) for the twin-line feeder cable was close to 460Ω.

A second test was made using the MFJ 269c antenna analyser to measure the twin-line feeder cable's inductance and capacitance, which were 18µH and 83pF respectfully. These measurements enabled an indication of the charac-teristic impedance (Zo) to be calculated by using Equation 3:

$$Zo(\Omega) \approx \sqrt{\frac{L}{C}} \approx \sqrt{\frac{18\mu H}{83pF}} = 465\Omega$$

(3)

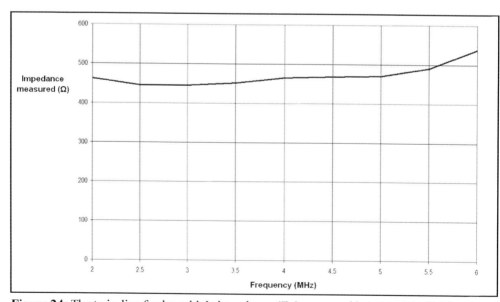

Figure 24: The twin-line feeder cable's impedance (Zo) measured between 2 to 6MHz.

A third test was made at 2.5MHz using a variable resistive load as the twin-line feeder cable's termination. The MFJ 269c antenna analyser was used to measure the SWR referred to 460Ω, with the resistive load termination changed from 100Ω to 850Ω in steps of 50Ω. This test showed the lowest SWR was when the resistive load was between 450Ω to 500Ω, indicating Zo was between these values, helping to confirm the previous measurements made. **Figure 25** shows the SWR results obtained from the measurements taken compared to the SWR for a theoretical resistive load referred to 460Ω.

It was not possible to make a direct measurement of the twin-line feeder cable's loss using the MFJ 269c antenna analyser. This was because, at 8m in length, the twin-line feeder cable was not long enough for the analyser to register a measurement. However, the MFJ 269c antenna analyser indicated an SWR of 3.1:1 when directly terminated with a 150Ω resistor when referred to 460Ω. With the 150Ω resistor then used to terminate the twin-line feeder cable, the SWR measured at its input was 2.9:1. Using the SWR alignment chart for determining a transmission line's loss (shown previously in Figure 20), a careful comparison between the SWRs indicated the cable's loss to

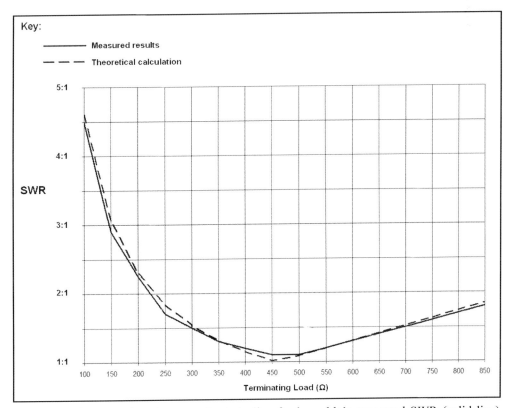

Figure 25: A comparison between the twin-line feeder cable's measured SWR (solid line) compared the theoretical SWR (broken line) when Zo is 460Ω when the terminating load varies from 100Ω to 850Ω.

around 0.1dB.

The twin-line cable has been used to feed a 20m long doublet antenna, enabling various contacts to be made. The transmit power level used was up to 100 watts, with operation from 3.5 to 28.5MHz. However, if higher power levels are required, a cable with a wider spacing between the conductors should be considered.

4.2 Coaxial Feeder Cable

Coaxial feeder cable has advantages that make it very practical for efficient operation in the HF, VHF and UHF bands. Coaxial cable has a minimal radiation loss because the outer conductor surrounds the inner conductor and so screens it. Therefore, because there is little radiation loss, nearby metallic objects have a minimum effect on a coaxial cable because the outer conductor serves as a shield for the inner conductor. Electromagnetic waves tend to propagate along the surface of a coaxial cable's conductors, rather than their inside, due to skin-effect [3]. Therefore, a coaxial cable's performance depends upon the resistance of the outer shield's inner conductive surface and the inside conductor's outer surface, which are functions of the conductors' sizes.

The inside conductor of a coaxial cable may consist of either a rigid solid wire, or several smaller strands twisted axially together. A stranded centre conductor improves the coaxial cable's flexibility, although tightly bending the cable can cause distortions (leading to problems associated with discontinuities). A rigid centre conductor maintains the uniformity of the coaxial cable's inner and outer dimensions and so tends to avoid discontinuity problems. However, this type of coaxial cable is not very flexible and can be difficult to install. The outer conductor of coaxial cable ideally should be made from a solid conductive pipe but this construction makes the cable difficult to bend. Therefore, to improve the achievable bend radius, this type of coaxial cable uses a corrugated outer conductor allowing the cable to be more flexibility.

Nearly all of the popular flexible coaxial cables employ braided outer conductors. Braided coaxial cables are not as electrically effective as cables with solid outer conductors because gaps in the woven outer braid conductor allow at least some signal leakage, or radiation, from the cable to take place. This can increase the attenuation of braided cables at higher frequencies. This effect can be minimised by adding a layer of conductive foil under the braid (this is often copper foil). Several examples of the internal arrangement of the concentric conductors for various coaxial cables used by amateur radio stations are shown in **Figure 26**.

The dielectric material used as the insulation, which separates the outer conductor of a coaxial cable from its centre conductor, determines the intensity of the electrostatic field between conductors and maintains the physical position of the inner conductor within the outer conductor. Common dielectric

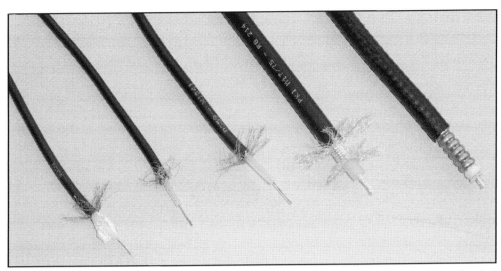

Figure 26: Five examples of coaxial cable. From left to right: 50Ω RG58 with screen/braded outer conductor. 50Ω RG58-mil. 75Ω RG59. 50Ω RG-214 with double-braided outer conductor. Corrugated 50Ω LDF2-50a. All shown with their outer sheaths removed.

materials for coaxial cable include polyethylene, polystyrene and PTFE. The dielectric material with the least loss is a pure vacuum, however the practicalities associated with using a vacuum makes its use impractical. As an alternative, dry air has similar electromagnetic properties to a vacuum and some coaxial cables use this as their dielectric material. The construction for this type of coaxial cable has the centre conductor supported using circular PTFE spacers equally sited along the cable allowing air to act as the dielectric between the conductors. Unfortunately, these air-spaced cables tend to have rigid constructions, making their use difficult, especially when the cable needs to be bent to run it around corners. The electromagnetic properties of gaseous nitrogen are also very similar to a vacuum and can be used by mixing it with low-cost polyethylene. This is accomplished by bubbling nitrogen gas through molten polyethylene dielectric material before the polyethylene solidifies. This material is often known as cellular polyethylene dielectric, foam dielectric, or poly-foam. It has half the dielectric losses of solid polyethylene at a low increase in the cost.

The characteristic impedance of most coaxial cables used in amateur radio installations is usually 50Ω. Other impedance cable is available and this is used, for example, for impedance transformers and baluns (as described later, in Chapter 5). The impedance of coaxial cable is often printed on the protective plastic covering for reference. In order to preserve the characteristics of coaxial feeder cables, special coaxial fittings are available for use when installing these cables.

4.2.1 Making Up a Coaxial Cable Feeder Cable

The concept of a coaxial feeder cable was previously shown in Figure 7(b) and its characteristic impedance (Zo) can be found using Equation 5:

$$Zo(\Omega) \approx \frac{138}{\sqrt{\varepsilon_r}} \cdot Log_{10}\left(\frac{R_s}{r_c}\right)$$

(5)

where R_s is the inner radius of the outer conductor, r_c is the radius of the inside conductor in millimetres (mm) and ε_r is the relative permittivity of the of the continuous dielectric between the concentric conductors (insulation).

Coaxial feeder cable construction example

Occasionally, it may be necessary to make up a coaxial cable to meet a specific requirement. This was the situation when setting up a dish antenna to enable operation on 2400MHz for the uplink to the QO-100/Es'hail-2 satellite. This necessitated a short length of coaxial cable to be made up to mount the antenna used to illuminate the dish (the dish feed). This arrangement needed to be clamped in front of the dish, without crushing the coaxial cable. In addition, with an operating frequency of 2400MHz, the coaxial cable's loss needed to be low. Consequently, the coaxial cable was made up using copper tubes of 6.5mm internal radius (R_s) and 2.75mm outside radius (r_c) with air acting as the insulation, giving:

$$Zo \approx 138 \times Log_{10}\left(\frac{6.5}{2.75}\right) = 52\Omega$$

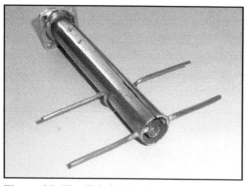

The tubes were soldered to an N-type connector, with the other ends connected to a dipole antenna. **Figure 27** shows the dish feed which was made up.

Figure 27: The dish feed made up for operation on 2400MHz using two copper pipes to form a 50Ω coaxial cable. The dish feed was held in place by clamping the coaxial cable's outer conductor, necessitating a robust construction. The slots shown form part of the antenna's balun.

Impedance Transformation

When a transmission line is terminated with a mismatched load, then a standing wave pattern is established along the line with the pattern repeating every λ/2, as previously illustrated in Figure 15. The value of the load impedance is repeated at every λ/2 null down the line, although the line's loss has a masking effect as the line length increases. Therefore, at its input, an electrically half wave (λ/2) long line will present an impedance which is equal to that of the load terminating the line. This effect is useful and is often used as an impedance transformer. An example of an aerial that uses this technique is the G5RV antenna.

If a λ/2 electrically long transmission line is terminated with a short-circuit, then the line's input impedance will also look like a short-circuit. However, an electrically quarter wave (λ/4) long line terminated with a short-circuit will present an extremely high impedance at its input. This characteristic of an electrically λ/4 long transmission line is the basis of how a line can be used, in effect, as a tuned circuit. Such lines are often referred to as "resonant sections". Examples of the use of this technique are often found as the tuned circuits for radio transmitters, receivers and filters operating at UHF or above.

If a λ/2 electrically long transmission line's termination is now made an open-circuit, then its input impedance will also look like an open-circuit (ie its input looks like an extremely high impedance). However, an electrically λ/4 wave long line whose termination is an open-circuit presents an input impedance that is extremely low (ie its input looks like a short-circuit).

Transmission lines, when used as tuned circuits, tend to be terminated in a short-circuit rather than as an open-circuit impedance because the latter tends not to be as reliable. If the transmission line is less than an electrical λ/4 long, then a short-circuit line behaves as if it were an inductor. Conversely, an open-circuit line which is less than an electrical λ/4 long behaves as if it were a capacitor. If the transmission line's electrical length is in degrees (θ), then:

$$\text{Inductive reactance } X_L\left(\Omega\right) = +j\left(Zo \cdot \text{tangent}\left(\theta\right)\right) \tag{20}$$

$$\text{Capacitive reactance } X_c\left(\Omega\right) = -j\left(Zo \cdot \text{cotangent}\left(\theta\right)\right) \tag{21}$$

Note

The term 'j' denotes an inductive reactive impedance and '-j' denotes a capacitive reactive impedance.

Figure 28 illustrates this concept for short-circuited and open-circuited transmission lines which are up to λ/4 electrically long.

The impedance at a null, or peak, of a standing wave is a function of the voltage and current at that point. Moving away from the null, or peak, the voltage and current will change in magnitude and phase angle. For a transmission line terminated with a short-circuit, over the first electrical λ/4 section from the

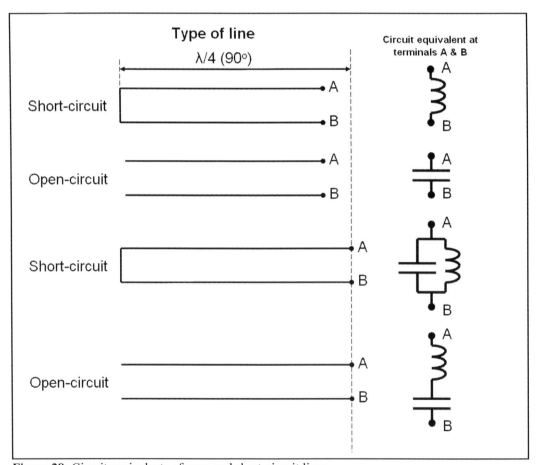

Figure 28: Circuit equivalents of open and short-circuit lines.

termination the line presents an inductive impedance. Then after the first electrical λ/4 section and up to where the line is an electrical λ/2, the line presents a capacitive impedance. The situation is then repeated down the line. If the line is terminated in an open-circuit, then this situation is reversed. This concept is illustrated in **Figure 29** for both short-circuit and open-circuit lines where the line length is in degrees (ie λ/4 = 90°, λ/2 = 90° and so on....) [7].

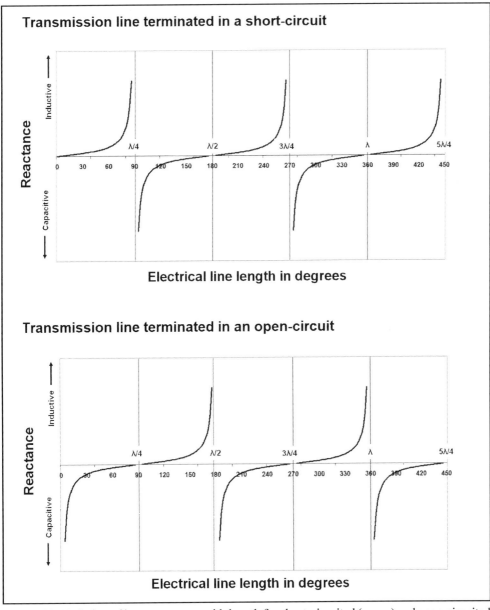

Figure 29: Variation of input reactance with length for short-circuited (upper) and open-circuited (lower) transmission lines. The sets of curves are identical and offset by λ/4 (90°).

5.1 Impedance Transformation using a λ/4 Transmission Line

When a transmission line has an electrical length of λ/4 and is terminated by a load (Z_L), then the impedance presented at the line's input is the reciprocal of Z_L. This effect can be seen when Z_L is an open-circuit resulting in the line's input looking like a short-circuit. Similarly, when Z_L is a short-circuit then the line's input looks like an open-circuit.

An electrically λ/4 long transmission line behaves like a transformer and can be used to match the load to the feeder line when their impedances differ [7] [8]. **Figure 30(A)** illustrates a λ/4 long line, whose characteristic impedance is Zo, terminated by a load of impedance Z_L. When Z_L does not equal Zo, then the λ/4 line's input impedance can be represented by Z_{in} as shown in **Figure 30(B)**. When Z_L is greater than the line's characteristic impedance Zo and using Equations 19a and 19b from Chapter 3, then:

$$SWR = \frac{Z_L}{Zo} = \frac{Zo}{Z_{in}}$$

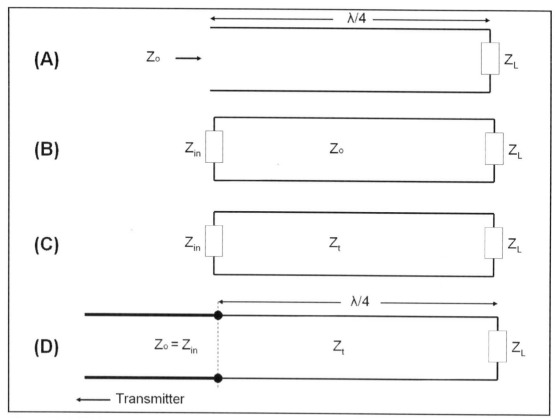

Figure 30: A λ/4 long transmission line of impedance Z_t can be used to match a transmission line of impedance Zo to a load whose impedance Z_L does not equal Zo.

Let the λ/4 line now have a characteristic impedance which is Z_t where this is different from Zo as shown in **Figure 30(C)**, then:

$$SWR = \frac{Z_L}{Z_t} = \frac{Z_t}{Z_{in}}$$

Rearranging this gives:

$$Z_t(\Omega) = \sqrt{Z_{in} \cdot Z_L}$$

If Z_{in} is now made the characteristic impedance (Zo) of a transmission line connected to the λ/4 line as shown in **Figure 30(D)**, then the λ/4 line's impedance Z_t can be found from:

$$Z_t(\Omega) = \sqrt{Zo \cdot Z_L} \qquad (22)$$

To summarise, a λ/4 electrically long transmission line of characteristic impedance Z_t can be used to match a load of Z_L to a transmission line of Zo, where Z_L does not equal Zo.

Examples
When Z_L = 110Ω, and the transmission line Zo = 50Ω.

$$Z_t = \sqrt{110 \times 50} = \sqrt{5,500} = 74\Omega$$

When Z_L = 200Ω, and the transmission line Zo = 50Ω.

$$Z_t = \sqrt{200 \times 50} = \sqrt{10,000} = 100\Omega$$

Usually, the value of Z_t for the λ/4 line works out to be a non-standard type of transmission line. Therefore, as described previously in Chapter 2, the physical dimensions of the λ/4 line could then be determined (using Equations 4 and 5) and a suitable line made up:

$$Zo(\Omega) \approx \frac{276}{\sqrt{\varepsilon_r}} \cdot Log_{10}\left(\frac{D_s}{r}\right) \qquad \text{for a twin-line cable} \qquad (4)$$

or

$$Zo(\Omega) \approx \frac{138}{\sqrt{\varepsilon_r}} \cdot Log_{10}\left(\frac{R_s}{r_c}\right)$$

for a coaxial cable   (5)

5.1.1 Example of using λ/4 Line Matching with an Asymmetric Antenna

A centrally fed half wavelength dipole has a feed point that coincides where the voltage is at a minimum and the current is at a maximum. This relationship, between the voltage and current, results in a feed point impedance of around 50 to 70Ω [9]. When the length of the antenna's wire span is increased at one end by multiples of an electrical half wavelength, with the antenna continuing to be fed at the same point, then the feed point's impedance rises to around 110Ω. As one side of the antenna is lengthened, then the radiation pattern is modified with more RF energy tending to be directed away from the antenna's longer end, so producing a directional antenna [10]. The concept of the asymmetrically fed antenna is illustrated as **Figure 31**.

The length of the wire span can be calculated using the antenna equation [11]:

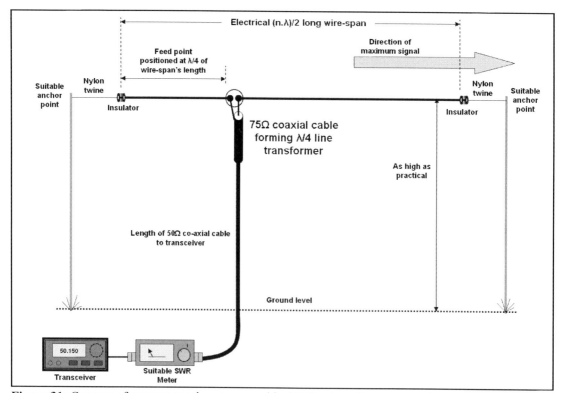

Figure 31: Concept of an asymmetric antenna and its λ/4 line transformer matching arrangements.

$$\text{Length (m)} \approx 150 \times \frac{(n - 0.05)}{f}$$

(23)

where n is the number of complete half-waves in the antenna and f is the frequency in megahertz (MHz). The antenna's feed point being located an electrical quarter wavelength (λ/4) along the wire span from one end.

Referring to Figure 31 and taking as an example a 6m band asymmetric antenna centred on 50.155MHz [12], using Equation 23 gives an 11.8m wire span length able to support four half waves (ie n =4). For the actual antenna, this wire span was made from 5 amp rated stranded plastic insulated wire and the feed point was located 1.4m from one end.

Matching Arrangements

With this antenna's feed point impedance being around 110Ω, if a 50Ω feeder line is directly connected to the feed point, this results in an SWR of around 2.2:1. Therefore, to improve the match, this necessitates an appropriate matching arrangement and a quarter wavelength (λ/4) transmission line provided a suitable option.

When an electrically λ/4 long transmission line is terminated by a load (Z_L), then the impedance presented at the line's input is the reciprocal of Z_L. This effect forms the basis to match the antenna's feed point to the feeder cable when these impedances are different. However, for this technique to work, the characteristic impedance (Z_t) of the λ/4 transmission line section has to be different from both these impedances.

The value of Zt (in Ω) for the λ/4 transmission line section can be calculated using Equation 22:

$$Z_t(\Omega) = \sqrt{Zo \cdot Za}$$

(22)

where Zo is the feeder cable's characteristic impedance and Za is now the antenna's feed point impedance (ie Z_L). Using a Zo of 50Ω and a Za of 110Ω, then:

$$Z_t(\Omega) = \sqrt{50 \times 100} = 74.2\Omega$$

Conveniently, RG59 coaxial cable has a characteristic impedance of 75Ω and could be used for the λ/4 line transformer. However, the physical length of the RG59 line is going to be shorter than λ/4 because of the coaxial cable's velocity factor. For RG59, the velocity factor is around 0.66c to 0.8c depending on the insulation used between the shield and the inner conductor.

Referring to Figure 31, for the 6m band asymmetric antenna, RG58 50Ω coaxial cable was used as the antenna's feeder and this was matched to the feed point using a length of RG59 75Ω coaxial cable as a λ/4 line transformer. Theoretically, the length of the RG59 λ/4 line transformer is 1.495m at 50.155MHz. However, its actual length was 1.2m and was found by gradually trimming the cable until a very low SWR was obtained (1.2m/1.495m indicates a velocity factor of about 0.8c).

5.1.2 Example of using λ/4 Line Matching with Two Yagi Beams fed using one Feeder cable to Produce Circular Polarisation

The polarisation of the antenna refers to the orientation of the radiated RF signal's electric field compared to the ground below the antenna. If the electric field is parallel to the ground below it, then the antenna is horizontally polarised. If the radiated RF signal's electric field is perpendicular to the ground, then the antenna is vertically polarised. In practice, when using a horizontally polarised antenna, this necessitates the distant station's antenna to be also horizontally polarised to maximise the signals received. Similarly, when the transmitting antenna is vertically polarised, the receiving antenna should also

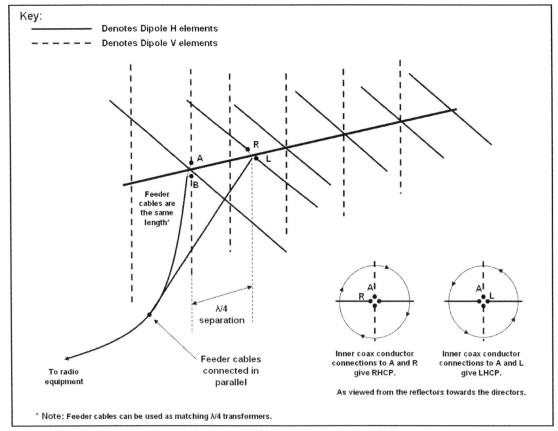

Figure 32: Concept of circular polarisation using λ/4 offset Yagi beams. Two λ/4 coaxial cable transformer sections are used to match the antenna to the coaxial cable feeder run to the radio equipment.

be vertically polarised.

However, there are situations where the distant station's antenna polarisation constantly changes making the use of either a horizontally or a vertically polarised antenna difficult. Where the polarisation of the distant station's antenna is uncertain, then a circularly polarised antenna provides a means to allow either horizontally or vertically polarised RF signals to be received or transmitted. An example where the polarisation of the RF signal is uncertain is when the distant station is a low earth orbiting satellite, where its antennas can rotate between being horizontally and vertically polarised.

One technique to obtain circular polarisation is shown in **Figure 32**, where two Yagi beams share the same boom support. One beam is mounted vertically (shown with dashed lines) and the other beam is mounted horizontally (shown with solid lines) as illustrated. One beam is fed 90° out of phase compared to the other beam and the effect upon the RF signal's polarisation is to cause it to rotate in a specific direction. A 90° phase difference between the two antennas can be introduced by positioning one Yagi beam a quarter wavelength (λ/4) along the boom from the other beam. This technique works because λ/4 is the same as 90°. Both the Yagi beams' dipoles are fed using equal length feeder cables whose far ends are connected in parallel to the feeder cable run to the radio equipment as shown.

Assuming each Yagi beam has a 50Ω feed point impedance and only 50Ω coax cable is used, then the impedance presented where the two equal length coax feeder cables are connected in parallel is 25Ω. This results in a poor match with the 50Ω coax cable run to the radio equipment, resulting in an SWR of 2:1. To reduce the mismatch, two equal length coaxial feeder cables can be used as matching λ/4 line transformers. This technique works provided the coaxial cable used for each λ/4 section has a different impedance to that used for the 50Ω coax cable run to the radio equipment. As described previously and rearranging Equation 22, the transforming effect is given by:

$$Z_{out}(\Omega) = \frac{(Z_t)^2}{Za}$$

where Z_{out} is the impedance presented to the 50Ω coax cable run to the radio equipment, Z_t is the coax cable's characteristic impedance used for the λ/4 section and Za is the antenna's impedance.

If coaxial cable is used for each λ/4 section, this has a characteristic impedance of 75Ω and the antenna's Z_a is 50Ω, then:

$$Z_{out}(\Omega) = \frac{(75)^2}{50} = 112.5\Omega$$

Figure 33: An example of λ/4 line matching used to match two antennas to the feeder cable run to the radio equipment. The antennas were two offset crossed seven element 70cm Yagi beams arranged to give RHCP.

Each coaxial cable λ/4 section now presents an impedance of 112.5Ω and these are connected in parallel. Consequently, the impedance now connected to the radio equipment's 50Ω coax cable will be 56.25Ω, giving an improved SWR of 1.125:1. Conveniently, RG59 coaxial cable has a characteristic impedance of 75Ω and could be used for each λ/4 line section. However, the length of the RG59 line is going to be slightly shorter than λ/4 because of the cable's velocity factor.

Sometimes, it is more convenient to use a longer length of cable as the line transformer section and it is possible to use an electrically 5λ/4 length of coaxial cable, however lengths greater than this should be avoided. This arrangement works provided the cable is electrically Nλ/4 long where N is an odd number (eg 1, 3, 5).

As an example of this λ/4 line matching technique, the following uses a circularly polarised crossed 70cm Yagi beam [13] as shown in **Figure 33**. This antenna comprised two offset seven element beams which were set at right-angles to each other. The antenna's design frequency was 435MHz (0.69m) allowing use on the satellite, FM and SSB segments of the 70cm band. Each Yagi beam antenna was arranged to give a measured feed point impedance of close to 50Ω. One beam was situated 172.5mm behind the other to provide a λ/4 offset (ie 90°).

For convenience, each dipole was fed using an electrical 3λ/4 length of RG59 75Ω coaxial cable soldered to the dipole's feed point to give right-hand circular polarisation (RHCP). The actual length of each 3λ/4 RG59 coaxial cable was 510mm and this included a 25mm allowance at the cables' ends to enable their connection to each dipole's feed point and to the 50Ω coaxial feeder cable. The two RG59 coaxial cables' ends were parallel connected with the 50Ω coaxial feeder cable in a 'T' configuration by carefully soldering their screens to either side of a small copper-clad PCB strip. The coaxial cables' three inner conductors were soldered together and plumbers' PTFE tape was wrapped around the inner conductors' joint, with the same tape also wound around the outside of the cables to protect the T-joint. Once completed, the T-joint assembly was covered in heatshrink as a protection against the weather.

The antenna was tested at 435MHz using 5W of transmit power. An SWR of 1.1:1 was measured, indicating a reasonable match between the antennas and the 50Ω coaxial feeder cable. The transmit power to the antenna was increased to 20W and an SWR of under 1.3:1 was measured from 432MHz to 437MHz. The antenna has been used for contacts through the Saudisat 1c and FUNcube low earth orbit satellites across Europe.

5.1.3 Example of using λ/4 Line Matching with Two Stacked Yagi Beams

When two identical Yagi beam antennas are stacked in the same plane, one above the other, the directional gain of the stacked Yagi beam antennas is higher compared to just using one of the Yagi beam antennas on its own. Theoretically, the maximum directional gain available by stacking two identical Yagi beam antennas is 3dB. However, in practice, stacked identical Yagi beam antennas typically increase the directional gain by around 2.5dB.

A major advantage of using two stacked Yagi beam antennas is that its turning radius is less than a comparable single Yagi beam of the same directional gain on the same radio band. For example, on the 2m band, a single five element Yagi beam antenna's boom is around 1.7m long and the antenna has a directional gain of about 7.5dBd. Stacking two identical five element 2m Yagi beam antennas, one above the other, increases the directional gain to around 10dBd and is comparable to a single ten element 2m Yagi beam antenna. However, a ten element 2m Yagi beam antenna's boom is around 4m in length. As a result this antenna's turning radius is around 2m, while for two stacked 2m five element Yagi beams, their turning radius is about 0.85m. Therefore, when the space to install a beam antenna is limited, the stacked beam antenna arrangement is an option to provide a higher directional gain antenna compared to using just one single identical beam antenna.

A drawback to using two stacked Yagi beam antennas is the antennas are operated in a parallel connection and this can create a matching problem with the feeder cable run to the radio equipment. For example, if both Yagi beam antennas each present a feed point impedance of 50Ω, when they are connected in parallel the impedance presented to a 50Ω coaxial feeder cable will be 25Ω, resulting in a poor match and an SWR of 2:1.

In a similar manner, as previously described for the circularly polarised antenna, two equal length coaxial feeder cables can be used as matching λ/4 line transformers to reduce the mismatch. An example of this technique

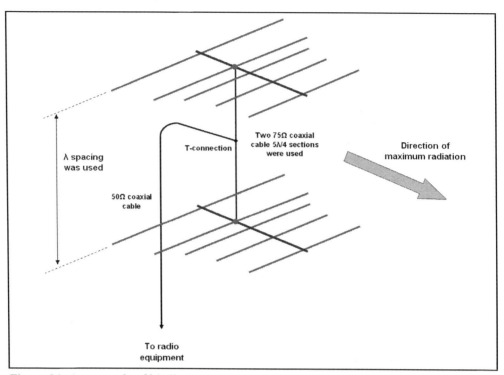

Figure 34: An example of $\lambda/4$ line matching used to match two stacked beam antennas to the feeder cable run to the radio equipment. The antennas were two 2m five element horizontally polarised Yagi beams spaced at 2m (λ) apart.

is shown in **Figure 34** for two stacked Yagi beam antennas.

This technique works provided the coaxial cable used for each $\lambda/4$ section has a different impedance to that used for the 50Ω coaxial cable run to the radio equipment. As described previously and rearranging Equation 22, the transforming effect is given by:

$$Z_{out}(\Omega) = \frac{(Z_t)^2}{Za}$$

where Z_{out} is the impedance presented to the 50Ω coaxial cable run to the radio equipment, Z_t is the coaxial cable's characteristic impedance used for the $\lambda/4$ section and Za is the antenna's impedance.

If coaxial cable is used for each $\lambda/4$ section, this has a characteristic impedance of 75Ω and the antenna's Za is 50Ω, then:

$$Z_{out}(\Omega) = \frac{(75)^2}{50} = 112.5\Omega$$

Each coaxial cable λ/4 section now presents an impedance of 112.5Ω and these are connected in parallel. Consequently, the impedance now connected to the radio equipment's 50Ω coaxial cable will be 56.25Ω, giving an improved SWR of 1.125:1. RG59 coaxial cable is suitable to be used for each λ/4 line section because it has a characteristic impedance of 75Ω, although the coaxial cable is going to be slightly shorter than λ/4 because of the cable's velocity factor.

Sometimes, it is more convenient to use a longer length of cable as the line transformer section and it is possible to use an electrically 5λ/4 length of coaxial cable, however lengths longer than this should be avoided. As described previously, this arrangement works provided the cable is electrically Nλ/4 long where N is an odd number (eg 1, 3, 5).

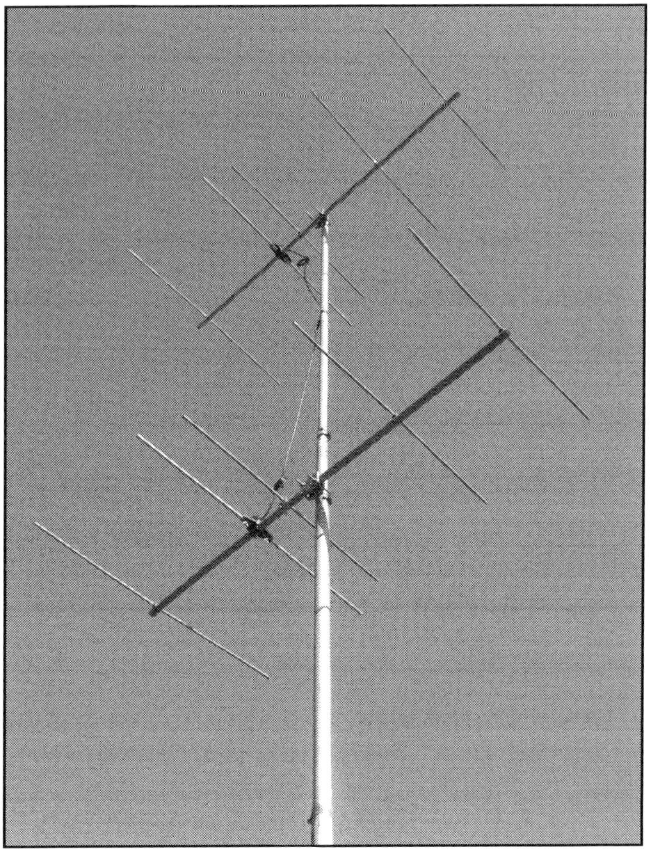

As an example of this λ/4 line matching technique, the following uses two stacked 2m Yagi beam antennas, whose concept is shown in **Figure 35.** The antenna's design frequency was 145MHz (2.07m) and each beam comprised five elements. Each Yagi beam antenna was arranged to give a measured feed point impedance of close to 50Ω. The two Yagi beam antennas were stacked in the same plane and spaced 2m (1λ) apart.

For convenience, each antenna's dipole was fed using an electrical 5λ/4 length of RG59 75Ω coaxial cable, whose physical length was 1.565m. This included a 25mm allowance at each end of the RG59 coaxial cable to enable its connection to each dipole's feed point and to the 50Ω coaxial feeder cable run to the radio equipment. The two RG59 coaxial cables' ends were parallel connected with the 50Ω coaxial feeder cable in a 'T' configuration by carefully soldering their screens to either side of a small copper-clad PCB strip. The coaxial cables' three inner conductors were soldered together and plumbers' PTFE tape was wrapped around the inner conductors' joint. PTFE tape

Figure 35: The actual stack comprising two 2m five element horizontally polarised Yagi beams spaced at 2m (λ) apart. 5λ/4 length lines connected in parallel with the coaxial feeder cable provided the match for this array.

was also wound around the outside of the cables to protect the T-joint. Once completed, the T-joint assembly was covered in heatshrink as a protection against the weather.

The antenna was tested at 145MHz using 10W of transmit power and an SWR of 1.2:1 was measured, indicating a reasonable match between the antennas and the 50Ω coaxial feeder cable. The transmit power to the antenna was increased to 50W and an SWR of under 1.3:1 was measured from 144.05MHz to 145.95MHz. The antenna has been used for many contacts during SSB/CW activity contests and generally for working local SSB stations.

5.2 Extending an Antenna's Frequency Range using the Transmission Line Equations

The doublet antenna provides a convenient solution to HF multiple-band operation, however there tends to be a practical limit to the lowest band which can be reliably handled by the antenna tuning unit (ATU). Therefore, the example described is where an existing doublet antenna, intended for use between the 40m and 6m bands, had its range extended to enable operation on the 80m band [14].

Doublet background

A doublet antenna comprises a wire-span which is centrally fed with a balanced two-wire feeder cable. Ideally, the length of the wire-span should be an electrical half wavelength ($\lambda/2$) at the lowest frequency of operation. Conveniently for this type of antenna, the length of its balanced twin-line feeder cable can be cut to suit the requirements where the antenna is to be installed.

The doublet's wire-span length can be determined using the antenna formula [11] below:

$$\text{Wire-span length (m)} \approx \frac{(150 \times 0.95)}{f}$$

where 0.95 is representative of the speed of the RF signal within the wire-span and f is the frequency in MHz. The wire-span should be installed as high and as far away from any close objects or structures as practical. Good practice is to run the balanced feeder cable vertically straight downwards from the wire-span where possible to the ATU and radio equipment.

However, there can be a problem when the wire-span's length becomes close to an electrical quarter wavelength ($\lambda/4$), or shorter, because the impedance presented at the antenna's input tends to be outside of the capabilities of some types of ATU to handle.

Loading a doublet

A loading technique can be used to allow a resonant $\lambda/2$ wire-span doublet (or λ/2 dipole) to operate below its resonant frequency. This technique involves adding a loading coil and an extension wire to each of the wire-span's ends to retune the antenna to enable its operation on a much lower frequency.

The existing doublet's intended lowest band of operation was 40m. Using an operational frequency of 7.055MHz and the antenna formula above gave the wire-span's length (in metres):

$$\text{Wire-span length} \approx \frac{(150 \times 0.95)}{7.055} = 20.2\text{m}$$

This wire-span was centrally fed using an 8m length of 300Ω ladder-line cable, with each leg of the wire-span being 10.1m long. This doublet has been successfully used for some time and its dimensions are included in **Figure 36**. The antenna provided the capability to work on all the bands from 40m to 6m using an ATU. However, on the 80m band the antenna presented a high impedance at the input to the ladder-line cable and this proved difficult for the ATU to handle.

The effect of the ground
When a wire-span is installed horizontally above the ground, the ground starts

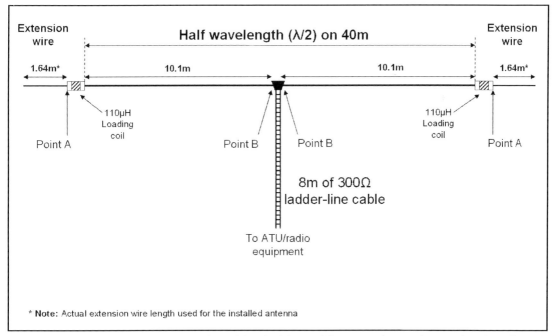

Figure 36: Concept of the loaded version of the doublet enabling operation on the 80m band. Each loading coil's inductance was calculated using transmission line equations in association with the extension wire lengths.

to behave as if it were the second conductor of a transmission line formed between it and the wire-span. Consequently, this 'earth-to-wire' transmission line develops its own characteristic impedance (Zo), where [15]:

$$Zo(\Omega) \approx 138 \times Log_{10}\left(\frac{4 \times h}{D}\right)$$

where Zo is the characteristic impedance seen at the wire-span's input, h is the height of the wire-span above the ground (in mm) and D is the wire's diameter (in mm). For the existing doublet antenna, the height h=7000mm (7m) and the wire's diameter D=1.6mm giving:

$$\text{'earth-to-wire' Zo} \approx 138 \times Log_{10}\left(\frac{4 \times 7000}{1.6}\right) = 586\Omega$$

This 'earth-to-wire' Zo becomes an integral parameter used in the following calculations.

Use of the transmission line equations
To retune the doublet antenna for operation on the 80m using this technique, it is necessary to add an extension wire and a loading coil to each end of the wire-span, as shown in Figure 36.

To determine the length of each extension wire and the inductance of each loading coil, it is necessary to calculate the quarter wavelength at the desired lower frequency of operation. Taking 3.65MHz as this lower frequency, then a 'free space' quarter wavelength (λ/4) is given by:

$$\left(\frac{300}{3.65\text{MHz}}\right) \times 0.25 = 20.55\text{m}$$

Referring to Point A in Figure 36
At 3.65MHz, the extension wire is going to be a fraction of a quarter wavelength (λ/4) and its end is open-circuit. Therefore, each extension wire-span is capacitive when viewed from Point A. Consequently, an indication of the impedance of each extension wire is given by using Equation (21):

$$\text{Input capacitive impedance } (\Omega) \approx -j\left(Zo \times cotangent(\theta)\right) \tag{21}$$

where Zo is the characteristic impedance between the extension wire and the ground (ie 586Ω from above), Θ is the line's electrical length (in degrees).

To allow for the velocity of the wave along the wire a correction factor of 1.05 has been used. The operator j shows that this is a reactive impedance.

To enable the antenna to be installed within the space available, each extension wire's design length was 2.3m in length. Therefore, Θ is given by:

$$\theta = \frac{(2.3m \times 1.05)}{20.55m} \times 90° = 10.577°$$

An indication of the impedance at Point A then is given by:

Extension wire impedance $\approx$ -j$\left(586 \times cotangent(10.577)\right) \approx$ -j3138Ω

Referring to Point B in Figure 36

Each leg of the doublet's wire-span is not an open-circuit because the end is terminated by an inductor followed by the extension wire. Therefore, each wire-span leg is inductive when viewed from Point B. Consequently, at 3.65MHz, the impedance at Point B can be determined using Equation 20 where each wire-span's leg is 10.1m long:

Input inductive impedance $(\Omega) \approx$ +j$\left(Zo \times tangent(\theta)\right)$ (20)

Here Θ is given by:

$$\theta = \frac{(10.1m \times 1.05)}{20.55m} \times 90° = 46.445°$$

Wire-span leg impedance $\approx$ -j$\left(586 \times tangent(46.445)\right) \approx$ +j616Ω

Determining each Loading coil's inductance

An indication of each loading coil's inductance (X_L) can now be found as follows:

$$X_L \approx -1 \times (+j616 + -j3138) = +j2522\Omega$$

(**Note**: This equation gives an inductive reactive impedance.)

An indication of the inductance (L) can then found using:

$$L(H) \approx \frac{X_L}{2 \times \pi \times f}$$

where f is the frequency (Hz) and L is the inductance (H).

Rearranging this equation allows an indication of each loading coil's inductance (X_L) to be found:

$$L(H) \approx \frac{2522}{2 \times \pi \times 3.65MHz} \approx 110\mu H$$

Loading coil construction

Determining the turns required for each loading coil is outside of the scope of this book. However, each loading coil was wound onto a 40mm diameter PVC white tube of 180mm in length. Each winding was 120mm long and used 94 turns of plastic insulated stranded copper wire whose outside diameter was 1.28mm. Each loading coil was checked using an MFJ antenna analyser and the number of turns varied to obtain an inductance close to 110µH.

Testing and tuning

Initially, the extension wires connected to the loading coils at each end of the doublet's wire-span were 2.3m in length. The antenna's resonance was checked by connecting an MFJ antenna analyser to the end of the 300Ω ladder-line and found to be 3.47MHz. Each extension wire was shortened to 1.64m increasing the resonant frequency to 3.52MHz. Most of this station's 80m QSOs are made in this portion of the band and it was decided to leave the antenna centred on 3.52MHz (Note: the bandwidth measured between the 2:1 SWR points was only about ±30kHz).

Transmission Lines, Antennas and their Interconnection

6

Twin-line feeder cables, eg ladder-lines, are symmetrically constructed and the currents flowing in each conductor are equal but opposite under ideal conditions. Therefore, little radiation takes place from this type of feeder cable and the cable tends not to be susceptible to picking up RF signals when on receive. This balanced mode of transmission is often referred to as the *differential mode*.

Taking as an example an ideal symmetrical horizontal HF dipole which is centrally fed, this antenna's theoretical electric field pattern is shown in **Figure 37**. This image shows the electric field lines equally aligned around the opposite halves of the dipole. Only the electric field lines have been shown for

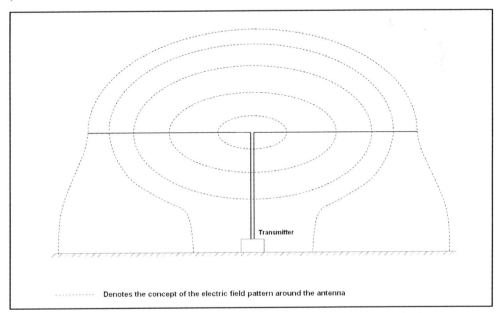

Transmitter

- - - - - - Denotes the concept of the electric field pattern around the antenna

Figure 37: Concept of the theoretical electric field pattern around a symmetrical antenna.

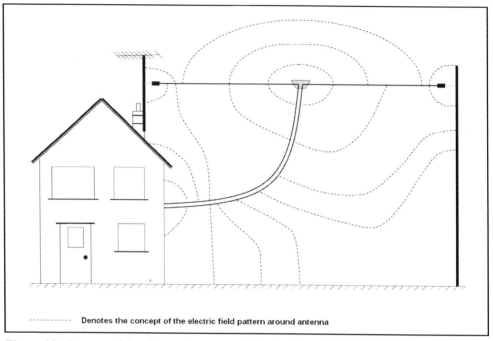

-------- Denotes the concept of the electric field pattern around antenna

Figure 38: Concept of the distorted electric field pattern around an antenna.

clarity in Figure 37, however the lines of magnetic flux also loop evenly around the dipole's wires as well. For this antenna, everything is symmetrical and the system is 'balanced' with respect to ground.

However, in reality, the antenna's electric field connects with the feeder, the ground, buildings and other objects nearby. The effect of this is to distort the electric field around the antenna as shown conceptually in **Figure 38**. Only the electric field lines have been shown for clarity in Figure 38 and there will also be a similar effect on the lines of magnetic flux. This distorted electric field induces RF currents into the twin-line feeder cable and this causes the currents flowing in the feeder's conductors to become unbalanced. This can result in undesirable RF radiation by the feeder cable, which is a potential cause of interference, can modify the antenna's radiation pattern and lead to problems associated with RF in the 'shack'. When on receive, any imbalance to the currents flowing in the twin-line feeder cable can allow RF noise to be picked up and impair the signal being received.

As a result, actual antennas can be very susceptible to the way they are installed, and are rarely well balanced. To minimise this unbalanced effect, an antenna should be installed as high and as clear of local objects as possible. This maximises the electromagnetic coupling between the antenna's opposite halves improving its balance and so reducing these undesirable effects.

6.1 Common Mode Currents and Their Reduction

It seems reasonable that using coaxial cable should overcome problems associated with the effect of unbalance because this type of cable has an outer conductive shield which screens the inner conductor throughout the cable's length. The two concentric conductors are closely coupled along their entire length, so the currents flowing in the inner conductor (I_1) and on the inside surface of the shield (I_2) are equal but opposite (ie *differential mode*).

However, coaxial cable is inherently unbalanced because of its construction, which uses two concentric conductors whose diameters are unequal. Skin-effect [3] causes the inner and outer surfaces of the coaxial cable's shield to behave as if they were two entirely independent conductors. The outside of the shield is, in effect, not coupled to the antenna in the same way as its inner surface and inner conductor. This results in a situation where there can be a difference between the currents flowing in the antenna at either side of the feed point. Skin effect means that current I_2 flows along the inside of the screen. When reaching the feed point, I_2 now has two paths it can flow into: either the antenna, or the outside of the shield. If the shield's outside impedance is low enough, then the current flowing down the shield can be significant. This is termed a *common mode current* and shown as I_3 in **Figure 39**.

With current I_3 flowing down the outside of the coaxial cable's shield, the feeder cable becomes part of the radiating antenna. This results in the problems previously described in terms of the distortion of the antenna's radiation pattern, RF currents on metal masts/booms and possible problems with 'RF in the shack' associated with running high power. To obtain an indication of the level of common mode current (I_3) flowing along a coaxial cable's outer conductor, this can be measured by using a clip-on RF current meter.

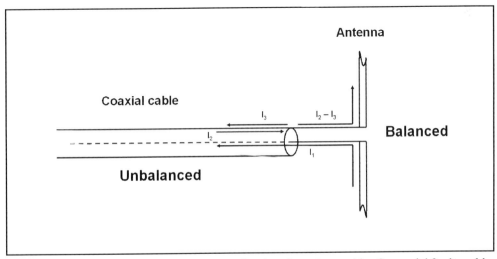

Figure 39: Concept of common mode current flowing along the outside of a coaxial feeder cable.

To minimise the undesirable effects associated with common mode currents, the primary technique is to reduce common mode current I_3 to a level where its effects become negligible. Essentially, when an unbalanced feeder cable is to be connected to a balanced aerial's feed point, then an 'unbalanced to balanced' transition is used and is called a *balun*.

6.2 Choke or Current Baluns

As described previously, the outside of the coaxial cable's shield can be thought of as a separate conductor which allows a common mode current (I_3) to flow. One technique used to minimise I_3 from flowing down the coaxial cable feeder shield's 'outer surface' is to add sufficient inductance to increase the impedance of this path. This is technique is the basis of the current choke or balun.

Often a current choke is formed in the actual coaxial cable used to feed the antenna. Consequently, within the operating range of the current choke, no impedance transformation takes place and often this arrangement is referred to as a 1:1 balun. For example, if 50Ω characteristic impedance coaxial cable is used to form a choke balun, then the impedance of the load (which could be an antenna) should also be 50Ω.

6.2.1 HF Choke 1:1 Baluns

An HF current choke 1:1 balun can be made from several turns of the coaxial cable which are wound into loops to form an inductor. A typical choke 1:1 balun is shown in **Figure 40** and comprises several loops of the cable of between 300 to 600mm in diameter which are held together using cable ties. Unfortunately, the high-frequency performance of this type of choke balun is affected by the distributed capacitance formed between the balun's loops. This capacitance, along with the choke balun's inductance, means the arrangement is effectively a high-Q parallel resonant circuit at a specific frequency. For example, an HF choke 1:1 balun can be made by using 2.2m of thin coaxial cable (eg RG58 or URM76) which is wound into about five turns of around 125mm in diameter to form an inductor. This arrangement has an inductance of about 6μH, however the capacitance between the turns is

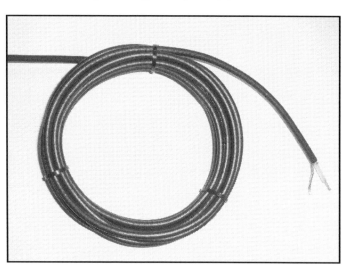

Figure 40: Example of a choke 1:1 balun for the HF bands made from coaxial cable.

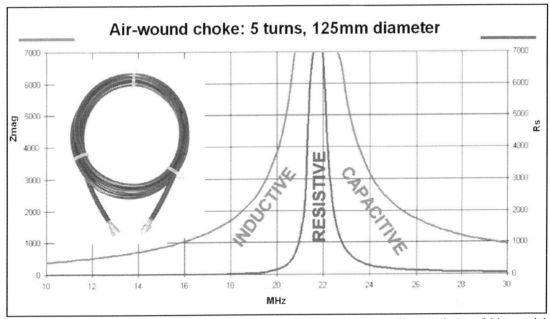

Figure 41: Performance of an air-wound choke comprising 5 turns 125mm diameter loops of thin coaxial cable giving resonance at 21MHz.

equivalent to about 9pF in parallel with the inductance. So instead of being a pure inductor, this arrangement is actually a high-Q parallel tuned circuit which is resonant at around 21MHz, whose measured impedance characteristics are shown in **Figure 41**. This has a tendency of making the choke 1:1 balun unreliable because its impedance is only high around its resonant frequency and much lower elsewhere. The resonant frequency can be sensitive to small changes affecting the capacitance between the turns, including even how tightly the turns are held together. Therefore, ideally this type of choke balun is only suitable for single-band antennas or where the spacing between the bands is narrow (eg 10m and 12m). The number of turns to be used depends upon the HF band in use, as summarised in **Table 2**.

It is possible to improve the frequency response for this type of HF choke 1:1 balun by adding ferrite cores [16]. This can extend the usable frequency range by about 2:1, enabling the choke balun to be used for more than one band. Essentially, adding ferrite cores increases the choke balun's impedance in terms of both its resistive and reactive components (ie R + jX). This

	Coaxial cable RG213/UR67		Coaxial cable RG58/UR76	
MHz	**Length (m)**	**Turns**	**Length (m)**	**Turns**
3.5	6.7	8	6.1	6-8
7	6.7	10	4.6	6
10	3.7	10	3.1	7
14	3.1	4	2.4	8
21	2.4	6-8	1.8	8
28	1.8	6-8	1.22	6-8

Table 2: HF single-band current choke balun construction summary.

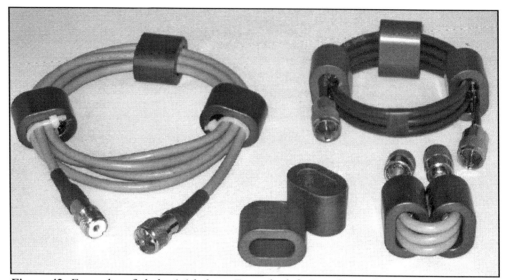

Figure 42: Examples of choke 1:1 baluns. From the left: Low-bands ferrite choke, mid-bands choke, high-bands choke, the ferrite cores.

in turn increases the impedance of the coaxial cable shield's outer surface, enabling common mode current I_3 to be suppressed to a low level. Ferrite cores also have the effect of increasing the choke balun impedance's resistive component, where it can exceed 1000Ω. A high resistive component is desirable because this minimises the heat dissipated by the choke balun due to the common mode current flowing (ie $I_3{}^2.R$ watts). Three examples of choke 1:1 baluns covering the HF bands which used Fair-Rite 2643167851 or Farnell 1463420 ferrite cores are shown in **Figure 42**, while **Table 3** summarises the construction details for these HF current choke 1:1 baluns [17].

High common mode currents (I_3) flowing along the coaxial cable's outer screen surface, associated with running high power, can cause other problems. If the current choke balun's resistive component is too low it can allow a significant residual level of I_3 to flow, causing the ferrite to heat up. If the choke balun has successfully suppressed the common mode current then the residual value of I_3 will be very low and it is unlikely that there will be significant

Band category	Frequency	Broadband choke details
Low Bands	1.8 to 3.8MHz	2 or 3 ferrite cores threaded onto a 5-turn coaxial cable coil of about 125mm diameter
Mid Bands	5, 7 and 10MHz	3 ferrite cores threaded onto a 5-turn coaxial cable coil of about 85mm diameter
High Bands	14 to 30MHz	2 ferrite cores which are super-glued together side-by-side and threaded onto a 3-turn coaxial cable coil

Table 3: HF Multi-band current choke balun construction summary.

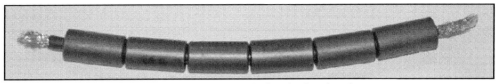

Figure 43: Example of an HF sleeve choke 1:1 balun for low band use.

heating of the ferrite. However, if choke balun has not significantly reduced I_3 enough, the ferrite loaded choke may begin to overheat. If this happens, the ferrite could reach the Curie temperature at which its magnetic permeability collapses, allowing I_3 to undesirably increase and cause further overheating of the ferrite. When using high power, ferrite choke baluns with a resistive component of less than 1000Ω are at a greater risk of under performing and overheating. Therefore, it is worth checking the manufacturer's specification when considering the use of some commercially available HF current choke balun types to ensure that they are capable of handling the level of I_3 expected of them. This is because many of these current choke balun designs were based on a resistive component of 500Ω, a value which can be inadequate if I_3 becomes too high. To make a good ferrite choke balun, the right grade of ferrite needs to be used which is able to introduce a sufficient loss at the operating frequency to minimise I_3 and make its effect negligible. Additionally, for the current choke balun to work successfully, it must have the right amount of coupling between the ferrite material and the magnetic field around the cable.

Another technique is to thread the coaxial cable through a series of ferrite rings to form a sleeve current choke 1:1 balun. Each ferrite ring can usually only take one 'turn' of the coaxial cable and so contributes a low inductive impedance (one pass through the centre hole is equal to one turn). Therefore, to obtain an effective sleeve current choke 1:1 balun this requires several ferrite rings to be threaded in series. This type of current choke balun works by presenting a high impedance to common mode currents (I_3) on the outside of the coaxial cable. An example of a 1:1 low band sleeve current choke using six ferrite rings is shown in **Figure 43**. This arrangement gave an impedance of greater than 2000Ω over a frequency range of 1.5 to 8MHz. However, for mid-band and high-band HF frequencies, twenty to forty ferrite rings may be necessary to provide an impedance exceeding 1000Ω to sufficiently minimise I_3 [17] as used by some commercially available baluns which are made up in this manner.

6.2.2 Choke 1:1 Baluns for the VHF/UHF Bands

As described previously, the outside of the coaxial cable's shield can be thought of as a separate conductor which allows common mode current I_3 to flow. If the impedance of this conductor is high, then I_3 can be minimised. A method to do this is to add inductance to increase the impedance of the shield's 'outer sur-

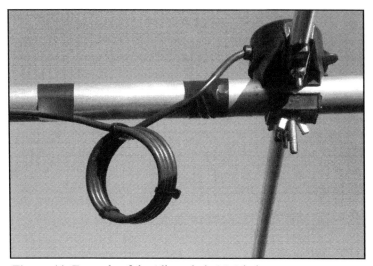

Figure 44: Example of the 'dirty choke' 1:1 balun.

face' conductor. This form of current choke balun is often formed in the coaxial cable used to feed the antenna. As a result, within the operating range of the current choke, no impedance transformation takes place and often this arrangement is referred to as a 1:1 balun. Taking a Yagi beam as an example, this can be done by winding several turns of the coaxial feeder cable to form an inductor as close to the feed point as possible to form a current choke balun. The windings can be held in place using cable ties, as shown in **Figure 44**. This technique works well from about 28MHz to 440MHz and this form of choke 1:1 balun has become also known as the *dirty balun*. For example, at 28MHz the current choke 1:1 balun is made from about 15 to 20 turns of coaxial cable wound onto a 25mm round former, while at 440MHz it comprises of around 4 turns wound onto a 20mm diameter former.

6.3 Other baluns suitable for use on the VHF/UHF Bands

A number of balun types, which are suitable for use on the VHF and UHF bands, depend on using a resonant circuit for their operation. Therefore, these types of balun are only effective over a limited bandwidth either side of the desired frequency (f) of operation. Consequently, this aspect needs to be taken into consideration when designing and constructing this type of balun. These baluns use the properties of either an electrical quarter wavelength ($\lambda/4$) or an electrical half wavelength ($\lambda/2$) long transmission line which is incorporated into their design, where:

$$\text{Electrical } \lambda(m) = \frac{300 \times \text{velocity factor}}{\text{Desired f (MHz)}}$$

(24)

Types of balun within this category include the sleeve 1:1 balun, Pawsey ($\lambda/4$) 1:1 balun and the 4:1 coaxial balun; these are described in the following sections.

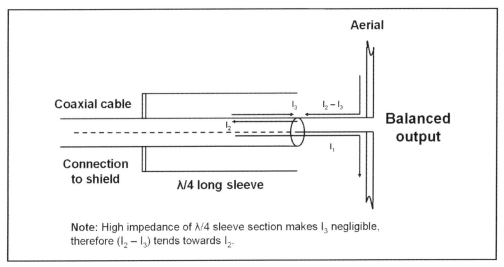

Figure 45 content labels:

Aerial

Coaxial cable

I_3 $I_2 - I_3$

Balanced output

$\frac{I_2}{2}$

I_1

Connection to shield

λ/4 long sleeve

Note: High impedance of λ/4 sleeve section makes I_3 negligible, therefore $(I_2 - I_3)$ tends towards I_2.

Figure 45: Concept of the sleeve choke 1:1 balun.

6.3.1 The Sleeve Choke 1:1 Balun

A transmission line which is short-circuited at one end presents a very high impedance at its open end when the line is electrically λ/4 in length. This property can be used to reduce common mode currents and forms the basis for the *sleeve choke balun* [18].

A conductive sleeve is slid over the outside of the coaxial feeder cable and concentrically connected to the coaxial cable's shield at a distance of an electrical λ/4 from the end of the cable as illustrated in **Figure 45**. The combination of the sleeve and coaxial cable's outer shield form a shorted λ/4 transmission line at the frequency of operation and so presents a very high impedance at the feed point between the outer of the coaxial cable's shield and the sleeve. The characteristic impedance of the transmission line formed between the sleeve and the coaxial feeder cable is not too critical, as it has very little effect on the coaxial feeder cable's characteristic impedance (Zo). It is the length of this transmission line which is crucial because this is the basis of the 1:1 balun. The ratio between the inner diameter of the conductive sleeve and the outer diameter of the coaxial feeder cable's screen should be from around 2:1 to 4:1, with air used as the insulation between them for the best results.

When the current I_2, flowing on the inside surface of the shield, encounters the feed point, then the high impedance presented by the λ/4 sleeve/shield combination forces most of current I_2 to flow into the aerial. The high impedance path presented down the cable reduces common mode current I_3 to a level where its effects become negligible giving a balanced match to the aerial's connection.

The coaxial line formed by the sleeve and the cable is an electrical λ/4 in length. If the insulation between the outer of the cable and inner of the sleeve

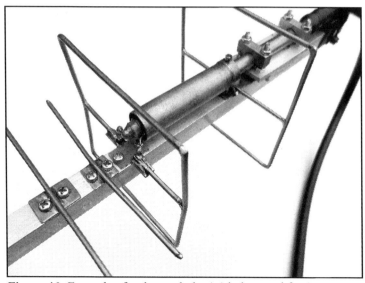

Figure 46: Example of a sleeve choke 1:1 balun used for 23cm.

is air, then the velocity factor of the cable/sleeve combination is close to unity and the actual and electrical lengths become very close. If the insulation between the sleeve/cable is the cable's outer plastic covering, then the velocity factor becomes more of an issue and the physical length becomes smaller than λ/4. This may require the sleeve choke 1:1 balun to be initially cut longer than required and then trimmed to tune it to the operational frequency.

Figure 46 shows an example of an air-spaced sleeve choke 1:1 balun used for a 23cm Yagi beam. The sleeve was made from 12mm diameter copper pipe terminated 57.5mm from the feed-point forming the λ/4 cable/sleeve line. This sleeve choke balun had air as the insulation between the sleeve and the cable allowing its actual and electrical lengths to be very close.

λ/4 sleeve choke 1:1 baluns provide a means to reduce common mode currents for VHF, UHF and SHF antennas, however their length for HF antennas makes them become very long and impractical.

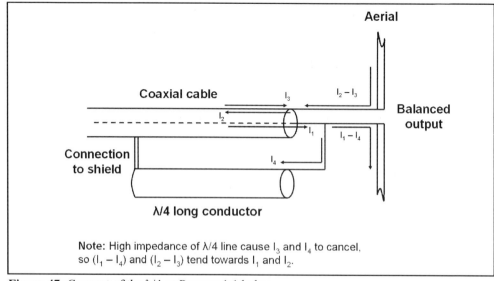

Figure 47: Concept of the λ/4 or Pawsey 1:1 balun.

6.3.2 The λ/4 or Pawsey 1:1 balun for the VHF/UHF Bands

Another 1:1 balun based on an electrically λ/4 long transmission line is the *Pawsey* or *λ/4 balun* [18]. This consists of a conductor run in parallel with the coaxial feeder cable of an equal diameter to the coaxial cable's shield. This conductor is connected to the feeder's shield at an electrical λ/4 with the other end connected to the coaxial cable's inner conductor as illustrated in **Figure 47**. The gap between the conductor and cable should be air making the actual and electrical lengths very close. Usual practice is to use a length of the same coaxial cable, as used to feed the antenna, with its shield forming the parallel conductor.

In a similar manner to the sleeve 1:1 balun, if the insulation between the cable and conductor is the cable's plastic covering, then the velocity factor can have an effect. This may require the balun's length to be initially cut long and then trimmed until the best match is found.

The shorted electrical λ/4 long line is connected between the coaxial cable's inner conductor and shield and presents a high impedance at the frequency of operation. This high impedance is connected in parallel across the aerial's feed point impedance (or radiation resistance), consequently it has very little effect upon the aerial's feed point because its impedance is low by comparison.

The central conductor's current I_1 flows into both the aerial and the parallel conductor as I_4. Similarly, the shield's inner current I_2 flows into both the aerial and the shield's outer surface as I_3. However, I_1 and I_2 are equal but opposite, therefore I_3 and the parallel conductor's current I_4 will also be opposite in phase. The transmission line formed by the parallel conductor with the coaxial cable's outer shield has its own characteristic impedance. This forces I_3 to be equal but opposite in phase to I_4 and they cancel, giving a balanced match to the aerial's connection.

Figure 48 and **Figure 49** show an example of the construction of an electrical λ/4 1:1 balun for a 2m Yagi beam's dipole. The balun's length was 510mm and made from RG58 coaxial cable. The parallel conductor was soldered to the coaxial feeder cable's screen (through a small

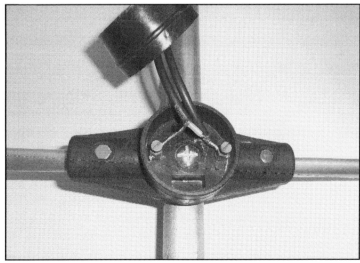

Figure 48: λ/4 or Pawsey 1:1 balun connection to a Yagi beam's dipole.

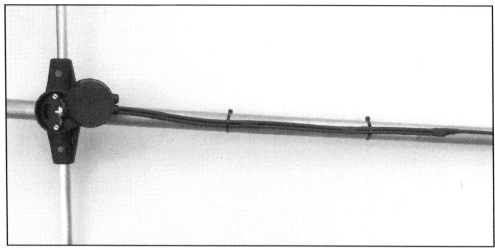

Figure 49: λ/4 or Pawsey 1:1 balun used for a 2m beam antenna.

access hole). Plumbers' PTFE tape was used to protect the joint and self-amalgamating tape was wrapped around the outside to weatherproof it.

This technique works well from about 50MHz to 440MHz, however for HF frequencies, the length of the balun becomes physically long, tending to make it impractical.

6.3.3 Coaxial 4:1 Balun for the VHF/UHF Bands

Another form of balun often encountered to match the feeder cable to VHF or UHF beam antennas is the 4:1 ratio balun which is constructed using coaxial cable. This balun is suited to use where the antenna's feed point impedance is high, as encountered with a folded dipole for example [19]. The 4:1 ratio refers to the relationship between the impedance seen at the balun's input and output. If the balun is made using coaxial cable with a characteristic impedance (Zo) of 50Ω, then the load connected to the balun's output should be 200Ω. Similarly, if coaxial cable with a Zo of 75Ω is used to make the balun, then the load impedance connected at the balun's output should be 300Ω.

Figure 50 shows the concept of the construction of a 4:1 coaxial balun. The balun is formed by adding an additional length of the same coaxial cable to the end of the coaxial feeder cable. This additional length of coaxial cable has a length of half an electrical wavelength (λ/2) and its inner conductor is connected to the coaxial feeder cable's inner conductor as illustrated. The coaxial cables' outer shield conductors are all connected together and this ensures that they are all at the same earth potential.

To explain the operation of the 4:1 balun [20] [21], consider a signal voltage is applied to the input of the balun and this gives rise to voltage V_1 at Point A as shown in **Figure 51**. Voltage V_1 is also applied to the input of the λ/2 length of coaxial cable and so appears at Point B as V_2. However, V_2 is a

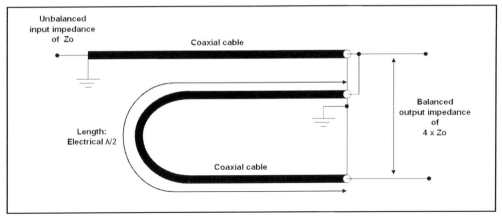

Figure 50: Concept of the construction of a 4:1 coaxial balun.

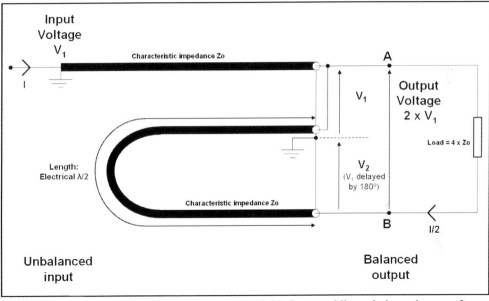

Figure 51: Concept of the operation of a 4:1 coaxial balun providing a balanced output for an unbalanced input.

version of V_1 which has been delayed in phase by 180° because the signal has had to travel around the electrical $\lambda/2$ long coaxial cable. Consequently, the relationship between V_1 and V_2 is such that their addition gives double V_1 across Points A and B as shown in Figure 51. This voltage (which is V_1 plus V_2 balanced across earth) is applied to the load, whose impedance is close to 200Ω and is connected between Points A and B.

The signal power applied to the 4:1 balun's input must equal the power delivered at the 4:1 balun's output (actually the output power will be slightly less due to cable losses). Accordingly, the current at the 4:1 balun's output will be half of that applied at its input, as shown in Figure 51. As a result,

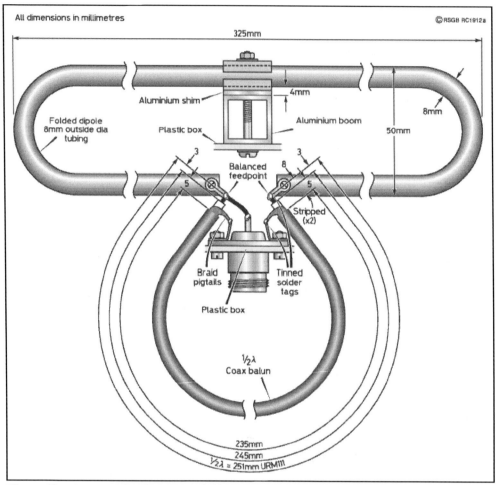

Figure 52a: An example of a 4:1 coaxial balun used to match a 70cm band Yagi beam antenna to its 50Ω coaxial feeder cable.

the impedance seen at the 4:1 balun's output will be four times that seen at its input. Therefore, the relationship between the balun's input and output impedances is 4:1 (ie 200Ω if the 4:1 balun is made using coaxial cable with a Zo of 50Ω).

The 4:1 balun's input is unbalanced, however the 4:1 balun has a balanced output by virtue of how the differential voltage across Points A and B is derived (ie $2 \times V_1$).

As described above, the operation of this balun depends upon a length of coaxial cable which needs to be electrically λ/2 long. This may require the balun's length to be initially cut longer than required and then trimmed until the best match is found.

An example of a 4:1 coaxial balun which was used to match the 50Ω feeder coaxial cable to a 70cm band Yagi beam antenna is shown in **Figure 52a**. In this arrangement the length of the λ/2 long section used was 251mm, including an 8mm allowance at each end to connect the cable. The coaxial cable used for the λ/2 long section was URM111.

Figure 52b shows another example of a 4:1 balun used to match a 50Ω feeder coaxial cable to a 2m band Yagi beam antenna, whose feed point impedance was close to 200Ω. In the example shown, the feeder cable and the balun were both RG58 coaxial cable. In this arrangement the length of the λ/2 long balun section was 860mm, which included a 25mm allowance at each end to connect the cable. Figure 52c shows the arrangement used to connect the RG58 coaxial cables together.

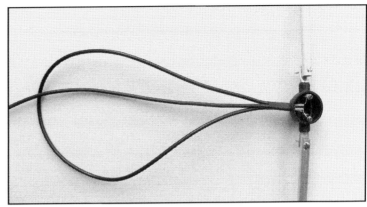

Figure 52b: An example of a 4:1 coaxial balun used to match a 2m band Yagi beam antenna to its 50Ω coaxial feeder cable.

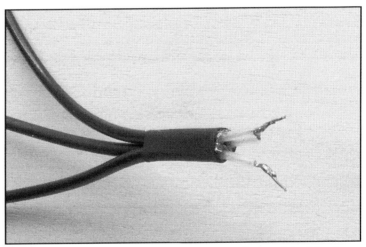

Figure 52c: The arrangement used to connect the coaxial cables forming the 4:1 coaxial balun used for the 2m band Yagi beam.

6.4 The Measured Effects of Common Mode Currents

The effect of using a balun to match the coaxial feeder cable to the antenna was assessed for a 2m band four element Yagi beam. An in-line current choke (*dirty balun*) was used for the assessment and was constructed by winding several turns of the coaxial feeder cable to form an inductor using the technique previously described in this chapter.

6.4.1 Antenna tests using a 2m Yagi beam

Two sets of measurements [22] were made using the 2m band four element Yagi beam horizontally polarised at 1.5m AGL. The results were plotted to provide an indication of the antenna's RF radiation pattern. The Yagi beam antenna was mounted on a tripod enabling it to be rotated through 360° and measurements were taken at 15° intervals by monitoring a distant test signal.

Initially, the measurements were taken with the in-line current choke situated close to the antenna's feed point. **Figure 53** illustrates the results obtained as a polar plot. A second series of measurements were taken with the coaxial feeder cable connected directly to the antenna's feed point. **Figure 54** illustrates the polar plot that was obtained for the antenna in this configuration.

As expected, Figure 53 shows the main lobe beaming directly forward of the antenna. However, Figure 54 shows how the beam has been skewed by about 15° to one side and the rear minor lobes have enlarged. This degradation to the polar plot has occurred because any common mode currents flowing along the outer surface of the coaxial feeder cable's screen allow it to act as an antenna. For both transmit and receive, any RF radiation associated with the coaxial feeder cable combines with the antenna's RF radiation to form an undesirable distorted field pattern as indicated in Figure 54. The two patterns provide a method to demonstrate the effect of introducing a balun between the coaxial feeder cable and the antenna's feed point.

During the tests, the SWR was monitored for transmit powers from 25W to 50W. With the coaxial feeder cable connected directly to the antenna, the SWR measured was 1.3:1. With the in-line current choke situated close to the antenna's feed point, the SWR measured slightly improved to 1.2:1 using the same transmit powers.

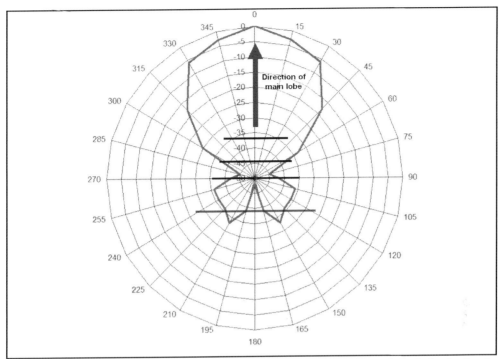

Figure 53: Yagi beam's measured RF pattern's polar plot with the current choke balun in circuit.

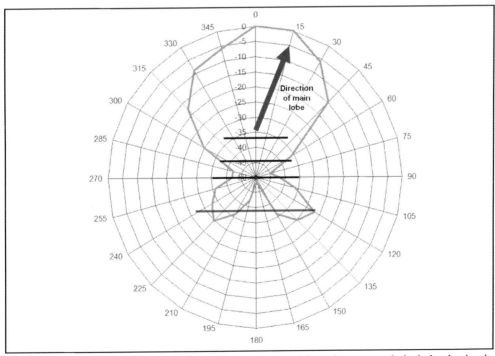

Figure 54: Yagi beam's measured RF pattern's polar plot without the current choke balun in circuit.

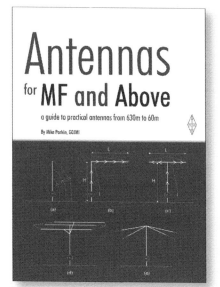

Coaxial Cables

A patent first describing a coaxial cable was granted to Oliver Heaviside in 1880 as British Patent 1407. This patent described the construction and use of a coaxially structured cable for telephone and telegraph circuits. The patent also outlined how conventional twin-wire cables, when run in parallel, can induce undesirable currents between them (often referred to as 'cross-talk' in telephony systems). The patent then described how this effect could be avoided if one of a twin-wire cable's conductors totally enclosed the other conductor by constructing the cable as two concentric tubes, with the inner conductor and outer screening conductor insulated from one another by a suitable material between the two running the length of the cable. The insulation material referred to in the patent was gutta percha latex or India rubber. The American Telephone and Telegraph (AT&T) company continued developing coaxial cables during the 1920s, resulting in Lloyd Espenschied and Herman Affel being granted US Patent 1835031 in 1931. This patent described the construction and use of coaxial cables for radio applications including television. This patent included clauses covering flexible coaxial cables and details of the attenuation when the ratio between the radius inner and outer conductors was 3.6.

7.1 Different characteristic impedances of coaxial cables

When using coaxial cable, two values of characteristic impedance (Zo) dominate availability: 50Ω and 75Ω. It may seem strange that there should be two common categories of coaxial cables, when it would surely be straightforward

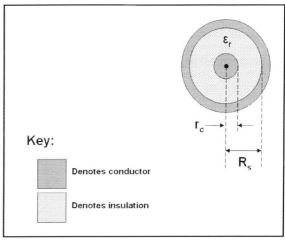

Figure 55: The parameters involved determining the characteristic impedance Zo for a coaxial cable.

Cable Type	Zo (Ω)*	Diameter (mm)	Velocity Factor (Vp)	Approximate Attenuation (dB per 30m)					Capacitance (pf/300mm)	Maximum operating Voltage (rms)
				1MHz	10MHz	100MHz	1,000MHz	3,000MHz		
RG-5/U	52.5	8.433	0.659	0.21	0.77	2.9	11.5	22.0	28.5	3,000
RG-6A/U	75.0	8.433	0.659	0.21	0.78	2.9	11.2	21.0	20.0	2,700
RG-8A/U	50.0	10.287	0.659	0.16	0.55	2.0	8.0	16.5	30.5	4,000
RG-9/U	51.0	10.668	0.659	0.16	0.57	2.0	7.3	15.5	30.0	4,000
RG-10A/U	50.0	12.065	0.659	0.16	0.55	2.0	8.8	16.5	30.5	4,000
RG-11A/U	75.0	10.287	0.66	0.18	0.70	2.3	7.8	16.5	20.5	5,000
RG-12A/U	75.0	12.065	0.659	0.18	0.66	2.3	8.0	16.5	20.5	4,000
RG-13A/U	75.0	10.795	0.659	0.18	0.66	2.3	8.0	16.5	20.5	4,000
RG-14A/U	50.0	13.843	0.659	0.12	0.41	1.4	5.5	12.0	30.0	5,500
RG-16A/U	52.0	16.002	0.670	0.1	0.40	1.2	6.7	16.0	29.5	6,000
RG-17A/U	50.0	22.098	0.659	0.066	0.225	0.8	3.4	8.50	30.0	11,000
RG-18A/U	50.0	24.003	0.659	0.066	0.225	0.8	3.5	8.50	30.5	11,000
RG-19A/U	50.0	28.448	0.659	0.04	0.17	0.68	3.5	7.70	30.5	14,000
RG-20A/U	50.0	30.353	0.659	0.04	0.17	0.68	3.5	7.70	30.5	14,000
RG-21A/U	50.0	8.433	0.659	1.4	4.40	13.0	43.0	85.0	30.0	2,700
RG-29/U	53.5	4.674	0.659	0.33	1.20	4.4	16.0	30.0	28.5	1,900
RG-34A/U	75.0	16.002	0.659	0.065	0.29	1.3	6.0	12.5	20.5	5,200
RG-35A/U	75.0	24.003	0.659	0.07	0.235	0.85	3.5	8.60	20.5	10,000
RG-54A/U	58.0	6.350	0.659	0.18	0.74	3.1	11.5	21.5	26.5	3,000
RG-55A/U	50.0	5.486	0.659	0.36	1.3	4.8	17.0	32.0	29.5	1,900
RG-55B/U	53.5	5.232	0.659	0.36	1.3	4.8	17.0	32.0	28.5	1,900
RG-58/U	53.5	4.953	0.659	0.33	1.25	4.65	17.5	37.5	28.5	1,900
RG-58C/U	50.0	4.953	0.659	0.42	1.4	4.9	24.0	45.0	30.0	1,900
RG-59A/U	75.0	6.147	0.659	0.34	1.1	3.4	12.0	26.0	20.5	2,300
RG-62A/U	93.0	6.147	0.84	0.25	0.85	2.7	8.6	18.5	13.5	700
RG-74A/U	50.0	15.621	0.659	0.1	0.38	1.5	6.0	11.5	30.0	5,500
RG-83/U	35.0	10.287	0.66	0.23	0.8	2.8	9.6	24.0	44.0	2,000
RG-213/U & UR67	50.0	10.287	0.66	0.16	0.6	1.9	8.0		29.5	5,000
RG-218/U	50.0	22.098	0.66	0.066	0.2	1.0	4.4		29.5	11,000
RG-220/U	50.0	28.448	0.66	0.04	0.2	0.7	3.6		29.5	14,000
Echo Flex 15	50.0	14.600	0.86		0.26	0.8	2.9		23.1	
UR70	75.0	5.800	0.66		0.5	1.5	5.2		20.1	
LDF4-50	50.0	16.000	0.88		0.21	0.68	2.5		26.4	
Westflex 103	50.0	10.300	0.85		0.27	0.85	2.7		23.4	

Table 4: Coaxial cable summary table. Note: * Zo = Characteristic impedance.

to standardise on one?

Referring to **Figure 55** and to Chapter 2, essentially for a coaxial cable where the internal radius of its outer screening conductor is R_s and its inner conductor's radius is r_c [23], then:

- Minimum attenuation occurs when Zo is 77Ω, where the ratio R_s/r_c is close to 3.61

- Maximum breakdown voltage occurs when Zo is 60Ω, where the ratio R_s/r_c is close to 2.72

- Maximum power handling occurs when Zo is 30Ω, where the ratio R_s/r_c is approximately 1.65.

Coaxial cables with a Zo of 75Ω are a good comprise when attenuation is a major consideration. Consequently, 75Ω coax cables were extensively used in terrestrial telecommunications line transmission systems where the distance between analogue repeater stations was a key factor (eg frequency division multiplex, or FDM, with working frequencies up to 60MHz). Coaxial cables where Zo is 75Ω are also close to the impedance seen at a half-wavelength dipole's feed point of about 73Ω and so eases matching.

Coaxial cables with a Zo of 50Ω, with a R_s/r_c ratio of 2.3, provide a good comprise between a Zo of 30Ω and 60Ω where power handling and working voltages are important factors (as found in higher power radio transmission systems). 50Ω coaxial cables have a breakdown voltage which is about 5% lower than the maximum when Zo is 60Ω, with a power handling capacity about 20% lower than the minimum when Zo is 30Ω. 50Ω coaxial cables have an attenuation which is about 10% higher than the minimum when Zo is 77Ω, making them also a reasonable comprise when attenuation is an issue.

Table 4 provides a summary of various types of the coaxial cables used in radio applications for reference [24] [25].

7.2 Joining coaxial cables together

7.2.1 Splicing coaxial cable
The radio engineer's method of joining two lengths of coaxial cable together is to use coaxial connectors. However, in the descriptions of coaxial cable splicing techniques to follow, it is shown that a splice can be made without connectors. A splice in a coaxial cable needs to be as close as possible to an uninterrupted run of the cable. In practice this requires four items to be considered:

- To maintain the required impedance through the splice.

- Have a short electrical length to minimise any discontinuities.

- Maintain continuous shield coverage.

- Ensure good mechanical properties (ie strong and waterproof).

Guidance on how to splice cables can also be found in the Radio Communication Handbook [26],

7.2.1.1 Example of G0JMI's splicing technique for RG58 coaxial cable

This technique, suggested by G0JMI, provides a means to splice two RG58 coaxial cables, or similar, together and the main stages involved are shown in **Figure 56** [27]. The coaxial cables were spliced as follows:

- Equal amounts of the coaxial cables' outer plastic covering was removed (about 30mm) exposing the braided outer shield conductor. The braided outer shield was separated out to expose the inner insulation on both of the coaxial cables. Then about 5mm of the inner insulation was removed, revealing the inner conductor on both coaxial cables. The cable centres were carefully soldered together (Figure 56A).

- A small length of the inner insulation was used to encapsulate the soldered joint. This was to retain the continuity of the inner insulation (Figure 56B). To hold the insulation in place, a single layer of plumbers' PTFE tape was used.

- The braided outer shield conductor of one coaxial cable was carefully drawn over the inner insulation, then the other coaxial cable's braided outer shield was drawn over this and the two were carefully rolled together. Spot solder joints were used to hold the outer shields in place (Figure 56C).

- Three layers of plumbers' PTFE tape were wound over the outer shields to protect the joint (Figure 56D).

- Heatshrink sleeving was passed over the joint and shrunk into place to seal the joint (Figure 56E).

The joint described above was used to join two coaxial cables to provide the feeder cable for a dipole antenna. The joint between the two coaxial cables has been situated outside and did not suffer from any degradation from being exposed to the weather during this period.

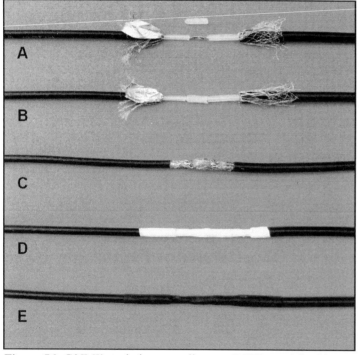

Figure 56: G0JMI's technique to splice two RG58 coaxial cables, or similar, together.

7.2.1.2 Example of GM3SEK's splicing technique for coaxial cables
These splicing techniques to join two coaxial cables together were suggested by GM3SEK [28].

Technique AB
For a coaxial cable splice the inner conductors need to be joined and insulated, then the outer shields replaced over this. When jointing the inner conductors, a large soldered joint should be avoided because this can create an impedance discontinuity over the short section of line giving it a different impedance from the coaxial cable itself. The neatest and electrically better way to joint the inner conductors is to use a 5-6mm diameter sleeve of thin brass tubing, see **Figure 57**(a), available from most model/hobby shops. To replace the dielectric, take a section of the original dielectric insulation, drill out the centre to fit over the sleeve, and split it lengthways so that it snaps over the joint, see Figure 57(b). To complete the splice, the coaxial cable's braided shields are drawn back over the dielectric section from each end. The braids are carefully soldered to avoid melting the dielectric underneath. For mechanical strength, a rigid 'splint' can be taped alongside the joint as a part of waterproofing it.

Technique AC
Alternatively, the splice can be made as a very short length of air-insulated coaxial line of the same characteristic impedance as the cable. The inner conductor is joined using tubing as already described in Figure 57(a). The outer is made from a short length of brass or copper tubing which is 'hinged' to fit over the joint as shown in Figure 57(c). Once assembled, the whole arrangement is then carefully soldered up. This method makes a very strong splice with good RF properties. For 50Ω air-spaced coaxial cable, the ratio of the outer to inner conductor diameters is 2.32 (ie R_s/r_c in Figure 55). Therefore, it is important to choose the right diameters of tubing for the inner and outer conductors to give this ratio. Remember that the relevant dimensions are the outside diameter of the inner conductor, and the inside diameter of the outer conductor. For UR67, RG213

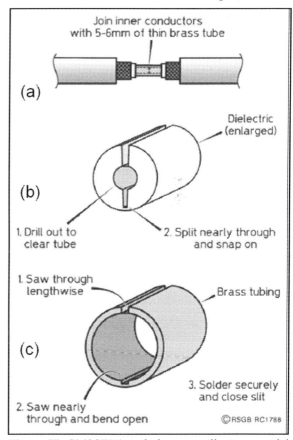

Figure 57: GM3SEK's techniques to splice two coaxial cables together.

and RG214 coaxial cable types, the best available tube choices are 8mm and 4mm outside diameters.

7.3 Coaxial cable RF connectors

There are various types of RF connector available for terminating coaxial cables. However, the three types which are commonly used in amateur radio are the 'UHF' (PL259), N-type and BNC. The type of connector to be used for an application depends upon the coaxial cable's size, the frequency used and the RF power level to be handled. When the connector is to be used outside, then a weatherproof type of connector should be used to protect the termination from the effects of weather exposure.

Coaxial cables commonly used in amateur radio are the American Radio General MIL 'RG' types with a characteristic impedance of 50Ω. These include RG213 which has a diameter of 10.5mm, RG58 which has a diameter of 5mm and M-RG8 (often known as Mini-8) which has a diameter of 6.5mm. M-RG8 is a compromise between RG213 and RG58.

When selecting coaxial cable, if there is any doubt about the quality of the cable then examine the braided outer conductor. This should cover the inner completely.

7.3.1 Tools for the job and their safe use

To successfully fit a connector to a cable, a few special tools are needed. Firstly, a suitable thermostatically controlled soldering iron is essential which is able to provide sufficient heat to solder joints properly depending upon the type of connector to be fitted. A sharp knife is also important for removing the cable's outer covering or cutting through insulation. A utility knife with a retractable blade may be necessary for larger cables, provided that a sharp blade is used. However, for smaller cables, a craft knife or a very sharp penknife could be used.

A junior hacksaw is useful to cut larger cables. A pair of small sharp scissors are needed for cutting braids, and a blunt probe (eg a darning needle mounted in a wooden dowel handle) is useful for un-weaving braided conductors. A scriber could also be used for this job. A small vice is useful to hold the cable/connector when being worked on. For most connectors, suitable spanners are essential to tighten the gland nuts. If it is intended to place heat-shrink sleeves over the ends of plugs for outdoor use, some form of heat gun should be used (a hot air paint stripper is not recommended).

7.3.2 Fitting 'UHF' connectors

'UHF' connectors include the PL259 'male' plug and the SO239 'female' socket. Most commercially available HF and VHF equipment use a version of the SO239 socket. Although called a 'UHF' connector, the PL259 connector can tend to become ineffective above 200MHz. This is because a constant system impedance (50Ω) is often not maintained through the plug-socket junction. Different versions of the PL259 are available for terminating RG213, RG58 and M-RG8

SAFETY FIRST

When using sharp blades, all cuts should be made away from you while keeping the object being cut secure on the bench and not held in your hand. Do not place excessive force on the blade because this may cause it to shatter and result in injury to the user or anyone else nearby.

When working with hot, sharp or delicate tools care should be taken so that accidents are avoided at all times. For example, wearing safety glasses when soldering, sawing or cutting is recommended.

---

cables to accommodate the difference in their dimensions. This type of connector is not weatherproofed.

Terminology Used

The techniques used to fit 'UHF' connectors to coaxial cables use the following terms:

- Cable's outer covering (sheath): the cable's outer plastic protective covering.

- Braid: the cable's outer conductor which surrounds the cable's inner. This outer conductor can be composed of closely woven strands that allow the cable to be more flexible.

- Dielectric: the material used as the insulation separating the outer conductor of a coaxial cable from its centre conductor.

- Centre Conductor: the conductor which runs axially along the centre of the coaxial cable.

Figure 58 (overleaf) includes a diagram showing the concept of these terms for reference.

7.3.3 Fitting PL259 Plugs

A) Without a reducer, PL259 Plug for RG213 type cable (also URM-67)

When fitting a PL259 plug to a RG213 cable, cut a clean end to the cable. This is a large cable and a practical way to cleanly cut it is to use a small hacksaw. When the cable has been cut, use the dimensions shown in Figure 58 to prepare the cable ready for the PL259 plug as summarised below:

1. First, remove around 27mm of the cable's plastic outer covering as shown in Figure 58, without disturbing the braid. This can be done by using a sharp knife and scoring through the cable's outer covering to produce a neat scored circle without disturbing the braid. A practical way to do this is to hold the knife and rotate the cable. Then run the knife along the cable from the score to the cable's end and carefully peel off the cable's outer covering. Examine the braid to check that it is shiny and smooth.

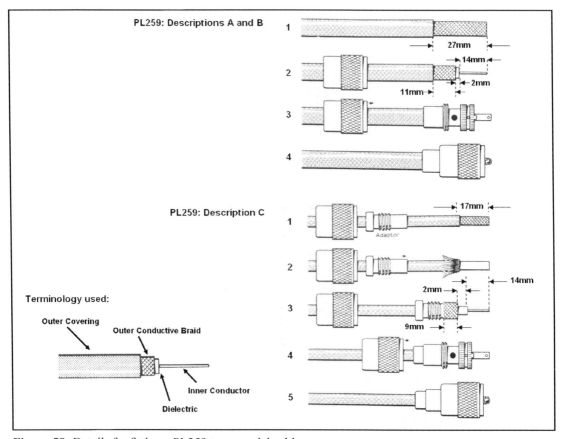

Figure 58: Details for fitting a PL259 to a coaxial cable.

If the braid has been disturbed, or it looks tarnished, start again further down the cable.

2. Slide the coupling ring onto the cable (make sure it is the right way round, threaded end towards the cable's free end). Trim the braid to leave around 11mm extending from the cable's outer cover. Remove the inner dielectric insulation, without damaging the inner conductor, to expose around 14mm of the inner conductor. With a hot soldering iron, tin the braid carefully with as little solder as possible. Also lightly tin the inner conductor at this stage.

3. If the plug's body is not silver-plated, then it might not solder easily so apply a file around the solder holes and also through them. Now screw the plug's body onto the cable until it is right down.

   a. When finished, the cable's outer plastic covering should have gone into the threaded section of the connector, the inner conductor should be poking out through the hollow pin and the end of the exposed dielectric should be flush against the inside shoulder of the plug.

   b. Look at the braid through the solder holes. If the tinning was successful, the braid should not have broken up into a mass of strands. Using a multi-range meter on its low ohms scale, check that the braid has not accidentally made contact with the plug's central hollow pin. If the braid has broken up, then it is best to start again.

c. When this stage has been completed, lightly clamp the cable to hold it steady ready for soldering, eg using a vice. Apply the soldering iron to each solder hole to heat it up. When the hole is hot enough, apply the solder and ensure that it flows into the hole to join with the tinned braid.

d. If the solder forms a blob, then possibly the plug's body was not hot enough. It is then better to use a suitable file to clean the blob off, clear the hole and start again. Once soldered, leave the plug undisturbed to cool before soldering the inner conductor by heating the pin and feeding solder down the inside. (Cooling may take longer than you expect, so do take care.)

4. Finally, when everything has cooled down, cut any excess protruding inner conductor and file flush with the pin, then screw down the coupling ring.

Note: The process described above is very similar for smaller diameter coaxial cables, where the PL259 plug to be fitted to the cable should have a smaller diameter threaded section.

B) Without a reducer, PL259 Plug for RG213 type cable (also URM-67)

There is an alternative method of fitting a PL-259 type connector which is often used by radio technicians. This involves removing the cable's outer covering and folding back the braid. The process is described below. Referring to Figure 58:

1. Remove about 27mm of the cable's outer plastic covering to reveal the braid.

2. Slide the coupling ring onto the cable (make sure it is the right way round, threaded end towards the cable's free end). Fold the braid back over the outer plastic covering to expose the inner dielectric insulation between the conductors. The dielectric insulation is removed to reveal 14mm of the inner conductor and this should be slightly longer than the PL259 plug's inner hollow pin. Next the inner conductor is lightly is tinned with solder.

3. The PL259 plug is then screwed onto the braid with the inner conductor protruding through the pin. When complete, the cable's braid should be enclosed inside the threaded section of the PL259 and not be protruding from the plug or into the inner of the plug. If necessary, unscrew the PL259 plug and slightly shorten the length of the braid, fold it back again over the cable's outer covering and screw the PL259 plug back on to the cable.

a. Using a multi-range meter on its low ohms scale, check that the braid has not accidentally made contact with the plug's central hollow pin. If the braid has broken up, then it is best to start again.

4. The inner conductor is soldered by heating the pin and feeding solder down the inner. When everything has cooled down, remove any excess inner conductor which protrudes from the pin, file flush with the pin and screw the coupling ring down.

This method needs no soldering of the braid, which can often result in a short. Pull-tests on correctly fitted connectors show that at least 25kg is needed to dislodge the braid.

Note
The process described above is very similar for smaller diameter coaxial cables, where the PL259 plug to be fitted to the cable should have a smaller diameter threaded section.

C) With a reducer, fitting a PL259 plug to RG58 or a Mini 8 type cable
If an RG213 type PL259 plug is fitted to a RG58-type coaxial cable, a 'reducer' is required:

1. First slide the outer coupling ring (the right way around) and the reducer onto the cable. Referring to Figure 58, next remove around 17mm of the cable's outer covering without cutting through the braid.

2. Using a blunt probe, un-weave the braid and straighten it a small length at a time until it fans out and surrounds the cable.

3. Remove the inner dielectric, without damaging the inner conductor, to expose around 14mm of the inner conductor. Tin the inner conductor with solder.
   a. Bring up the reducer until the end of the reducer is flush with the end of the cable's outer covering. Fold the braid back so it lies evenly over the shank of the reducer, then remove the excess braid with scissors so that it does not become trapped in the threads. Smooth down the braid and then offer up the plug body.

4. While holding the reducer and cable steady, screw on the plug body until it is fully home. It is possibly better to complete this stage using two pairs of pliers.
   a. Now hold the assembly in the vice and carefully solder the braid through the holes.
   b. Solder the inner conductor by heating the pin and feeding solder down the inner. Using a multi-range meter on its low ohms scale, check that the braid has not accidentally made contact with the plug's central hollow pin. If the braid has broken up, then it is best to start again.

5. When everything has cooled down, remove any excess inner conductor which protrudes from the pin, file any excess solder/conductor off the pin and screw the coupling ring down.

There has been some discussion whether it is necessary to solder the braid through the holes. However, radio technicians tend to prefer soldered connections from a reliability perspective compared to compression type connectors.

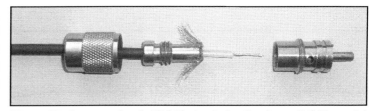

Figure 59 shows an example of this technique to fit a PL259 plug to an RG58 coaxial cable using a reducer.

Figure 59: An example of a PL259 plug being fitted to an RG58 coaxial cable using a reducer.

7.3.3.1 Cable continuity testing

For techniques A), B) and C) described above, use a multi-range meter set to its low-ohms range to make a continuity check to test both the inner and outer conductors from one end of the cable to the other. Also check that the inner conductor has not shorted to the braid. The plug assembly can be finished by adding a short piece of heat-shrink sleeving on the tail of the cable to seal it from moisture.

7.3.3.2 PL259 plug body variants

To enable PL259 plugs to be fitted to smaller diameter cables, there are versions available which have reduced diameter plug bodies. These connectors avoid the use of reducers and typically have plug bodies to accept 5mm and 6.5mm diameter cables. The process to fit these plugs is the same as previously described. **Figure 60** illustrates examples of PL259 plug variants suited to fit coaxial cable of various diameters.

7.3.4 Fitting BNC plugs

These are 'constant impedance' connectors because, when correctly made up, the system impedance (50Ω or 75Ω) is maintained right through the connection. It is important that the coaxial cable fits the plug correctly, therefore check that each part of the plug fits the cable properly when preparing it.

There are 50Ω or 75Ω types of BNC plugs available and the dimensions of each type of plug differ – but only very slightly to the naked eye. When fitting this type of plug it is important to make sure that the appropriate impedance type is used.

Figure 60: Examples of PL259 plug variants. From the left a PL259 front view, PL259 suitable for use with RG58 cable types, PL259 suitable for RG62 and RG59 cable types, PL259 suitable for RG213 cable types, weatherproof PL259 version suitable for RG213 cable types.

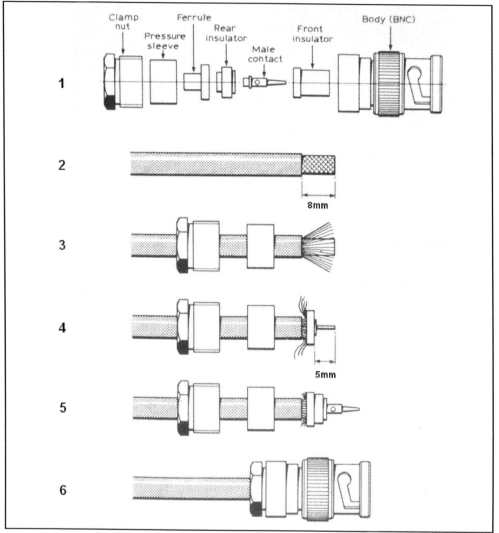

Figure 61: Suggested dimensions for BNC plugs and line sockets which use a ferrule.

The process to fit a 'male' BNC plug on to a coaxial cable is described for the commonly used 'ferrule' type as shown in **Figure 61**:

1. The general BNC plug's component parts.
2. Remove 8mm of the cable's outer covering. This can be done by using a sharp knife and scoring through the cable's outer covering to produce a neat scored circle without disturbing the braid. A practical way to do this is to hold the knife and rotate the cable. Then run the knife along the cable from the score to the cable's end and carefully peel off the cable's outer covering.
3. Slide the clamp-nut and pressure seal over the cable. Using a blunt probe,

un-weave the braid and comb it out.

4. Fold the braid back and slide the ferrule down over the dielectric insulation, then insert the ferrule between the braid and the dielectric insulation. Using sharp scissors, trim off the excess braid around the edge of the ferrule. Remove 5mm of the dielectric insulation taking care not to damage the inner conductor. With the soldering iron, tin the end of the inner conductor.

5. Slide the rear insulator over the inner conductor and locate the shoulder of the insulator's inside recess into the ferrule. Slide the centre pin (shown as the male contact) over the inner conductor until the shoulder of the pin is pressed against the rear insulator. Solder the pin to the inner conductor by placing the soldering iron bit (tinned but with the solder wiped off) on the side of the pin opposite the solder hole. Feed a small quantity of solder into the hole (typically 22SWG works well). Avoid overheating the pin.

6. Fit the front insulator and push the assembly into the plug's body as far as possible. Slide the pressure seal into the body and screw the clamp-nut tightly to clamp the cable. To tighten the clamp-nut, use a suitable spanner, while using a second spanner to hold the plug body steady to stop it rotating. Usually, spanners for working with BNC plug should be thin 3/8in AF.

7.3.4.1 Cable continuity testing

For the techniques described above, use a multi-range meter set to its low-ohms range to make a continuity check to test both the inner and outer conductors from one end of the cable to the other. Also check that the inner conductor has not shorted to the braid. The plug assembly can be finished by adding a short piece of heat-shrink sleeving on the tail of the cable to seal it from moisture.

7.3.4.2 BNC connector variations

Angle plugs generally follow a similar pattern to the straight types, except that connection to the coaxial cable's inner conductor is via a slotted pin, accessed via a removable screw-cap. Tighten the clamp-nut before soldering the coaxial cable's inner conductor. Line sockets are fitted in a similar way as the plugs.

Figure 62 illustrates examples of various types of BNC plugs and a socket, along with various N-type plug and socket variants, suited to fit coaxial cable of various diameters.

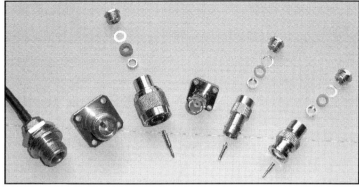

Figure 62: Examples of BNC/N-type plug and socket variants. From the left an N-type socket single-hole mount type, N-type socket, N-type plug for RG58 cable types, BNC socket, BNC in-line socket, BNC suitable for RG58 cable types.

7.3.4.3 General comments on fitting BNC plugs to cables
By using the instructions above as a guide, it should not be too difficult to fit a plug correctly to a coaxial cable. One important point to note is that if the plug has been assembled correctly and tightened up properly, the clamp-nut will have (intentionally) cut into the pressure seal. This often makes the plug difficult to re-use and may not to allow a second attempt. The thicker pressure seal plug types will often allow careful re-use.

7.3.5 Fitting N-type plugs
These are 'constant impedance' connectors because, when correctly made up, the system impedance (50Ω) is maintained right through the connection. It is important that the coaxial cable fits the plug correctly, therefore check that

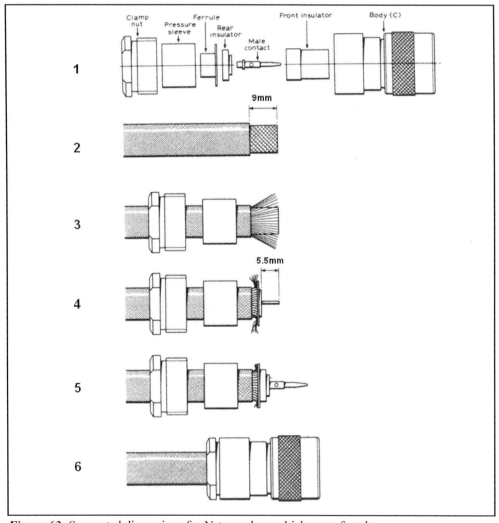

Figure 63: Suggested dimensions for N-type plugs which use a ferrule.

each part of the plug fits the cable properly when preparing it.

There are 50Ω or 75Ω types of N plugs available and the dimensions of each type of plug differ – but only very slightly to the naked eye. 50Ω N connectors seem much more common than the 75Ω type. When fitting this type of plug it is important to make sure that the appropriate impedance type is used.

The process to fit a 'male' N-type plug on to a coaxial cable is described for the commonly used 'ferrule' type as shown in **Figure 63**:

1. The general N-type plug's component parts.

2. Remove 9mm of the cable's outer covering. This can be done by using a sharp knife and scoring through the cable's outer covering to produce a neat scored circle without disturbing the braid. A practical way to do this is to hold the knife and rotate the cable. Then run the knife along the cable from the score to the cable's end and carefully peel off the cable's outer covering.

3. Slide the clamp-nut and pressure seal over the cable. Using a blunt probe, un-weave the braid and comb it out.

4. Fold the braid back and slide the ferrule down over the dielectric insulation. Insert the ferrule between the braid and the dielectric insulation. Using sharp scissors, trim off the excess braid around the edge of the ferrule. Remove 5.5mm of the dielectric insulation taking care not to damage the inner conductor. With the soldering iron, tin the end of the inner conductor.

5. Slide the rear insulator over the inner conductor and position it against the end of the dielectric insulation (the dielectric insulation should be just be protruding out of the ferrule). Slide the centre pin (shown as the male contact) over the inner conductor until the shoulder of the pin is pressed against the rear insulator. Solder the pin to the inner conductor by placing the soldering iron bit (tinned but with the solder wiped off) on the side of the pin opposite the solder hole. Feed a small quantity of solder into the hole (typically 22SWG works well). Avoid overheating the pin.

6. Fit the front insulator and push the assembly into the plug's body as far as possible. Slide the pressure seal into the body and screw the clamp-nut tightly to clamp the cable. To tighten the clamp-nut, use a suitable spanner, while using a second spanner to hold the plug body steady to stop it rotating. Useful spanners for working with N-types plug are usually 11/16 AF and 5/8 AF types.

7.3.5.1 N-type connector variants

Angle plugs generally follow a similar pattern to the straight types, except that connection to the inner is via a slotted pin, accessed via a removable screw-cap. Tighten the clamp-nut before soldering the inner. Line sockets are fitted in a similar way as plugs.

N-type connectors have evolved over the years, consequently there are

Figure 64: Partially assembled 'solder-less' N-connector used with Ecoflex 15 coaxial cable. Note that the centre pin is a tight push fit over the coax centre conductor.

a number of different types which may be encountered. These differences are mostly to do with the cable clamping and centre pin securing methods.

Many N-type male and female connectors used on high-grade low loss cables can be solder-less types. These include N-type connectors used with Ecoflex15 which is a high grade coaxial cable used at VHF/UHF, see **Figure 64**. This connector design can be more straightforward to fit.

Figure 62 illustrates examples of various types of N-type plugs and socket variants, along with various types of BNC plugs and sockets, suited to fit coaxial cable of various diameters.

7.3.5.2 Cable continuity testing

For the techniques described above, use a multi-range meter set to its low ohms range to make a continuity check to test both the inner and outer conductors from one end of the cable to the other. Also check that the inner conductor has not shorted to the braid. The plug assembly can be finished by adding a short piece of heat-shrink sleeving on the tail of the cable to seal it from moisture.

7.3.6 TNC and C-Type Connectors

TNC connectors are similar to BNC connectors and are fitted to cables in a similar way to BNC connectors. However, TNC connectors are threaded to enable the plug to be secured to the socket.

C-Type are similar to N-type connectors and are fitted to cables in a similar way as N-type connectors. However, C-Type plugs resemble large BNC plugs and the plug is secured to the socket in a similar way to that used by BNC connectors.

These connectors are also available in 50Ω and 75Ω versions.

7.4 Comparison of UHF with N-type coaxial cable connectors

PL259 plugs and SO239 sockets used to be known as UHF connectors. However, the capability of their use at UHF is often queried and is the basis for the following series of comparison tests [29].

Nowadays, the use of SO239 sockets on radio equipment is extensive and so necessitates the use of a PL259 plug to terminate the coaxial cable run from the antenna. Often these plugs and sockets are referred to as UHF connectors and this can be misleading, giving the expectation that they work well into the UHF spectrum (which extends from 300MHz to 3GHz). Originating from the

1930s, this threaded coupling connector was intended for use in video applications for use from 0.6 to 300MHz [30]. **Figure 65** shows examples of a typical four hole SO239 socket, a single hole SO239 socket, a SO239 coupling (or back-to-back) and a PL259 plug.

Figure 65: From the left, examples of two SO239 sockets, a SO239 coupling and a PL259 plug.

7.4.1 Calculated theoretical SWR for two 50Ω cables connected with PL259 plugs and a SO239 coupling

An indication of the impedance introduced by a PL259 to SO239 connection can be found by considering this as a transmission line which will have its own characteristic impedance (Zo). Using the coaxial cable characteristic impedance (Zo) Equation 5, as described in Chapter 2, it possible to calculate Zo for the PL259/SO239 connection:

$$Zo(\Omega) \approx \frac{138}{\sqrt{\varepsilon_r}} \cdot Log_{10}\left(\frac{R_s}{r_c}\right)$$

(5)

where R_s is the inner radius of the outer conductor and r_c is the radius of the inner conductor in millimetres (mm). ε_r is the relative permittivity of the insulation between the concentric conductors.

Using Equation 5 and making measurements of R_s and r_c for a single-hole and a four-hole SO239 socket gave a characteristic impedance of 34.6Ω, assuming PTFE as the insulation (using $\varepsilon_r \approx 2.1$, $R_s = 11.6$mm, $r_c = 5.03$mm).

To gain an indication of the effect of using PL259 and S239 connectors, the theoretical standing wave ratio (SWR) was calculated when two PL259 plugs were used to connect two lengths of 50Ω coaxial cable together using an SO239 coupling. For this calculation, the PL259/SO239 connection was likened to a short transmission line with a length of 36mm, an assumed DC resistance of 0Ω and a characteristic impedance (Zo) of 34.6Ω. This allowed the impedance to be calculated using Equation 20, where the connectors meet the 50Ω coaxial cables. This will give the PL259/SO239 connection an inductive reactance (X_L) because the coaxial cables can be regarded as not being open-circuit, as described in Chapter 5. Consequently:

$$\text{PL259/SO239 connection's impedance} \approx +j\left(Zo \cdot tangent(\theta)\right)\Omega$$

(20)

where Θ is the short transmission line's electrical length (in degrees). As the

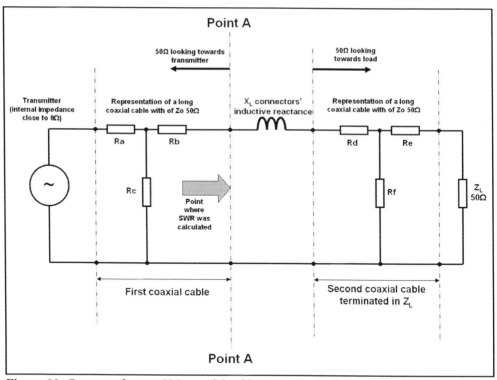

Figure 66: Concept of a two 50Ω coaxial cables connected using PL259 plugs and a SO239 coupling.

frequency increases, so the value of ϴ will change because the transmission line's electrical length increases. Consequently, the theoretical value calculated for the PL259/SO239 connection's inductive reactance (X_L) will increase.

The PL259/SO239 connection can be thought of as an inductor (X_L) in series between the two coaxial cables as shown conceptually in **Figure 66** where the two coaxial cables are represented as attenuators. The first coaxial cable is represented by resistors Ra, Rb and Rc which form a low loss attenuator with an impedance of 50Ω, which is connected to the transmitter as shown. The second coaxial cable is represented by resistors Rd, Re and Rf which form another low loss attenuator also with an impedance of 50Ω, which is terminated by a load Z_L of 50Ω.

Consequently, the combination of the PL259/SO239 connectors (ie X_L) and the second coaxial cable can be thought of presenting an impedance which terminates the first coaxial cable where:

Impedance connected to first coaxial cable = 50Ω + jX_L.

As the operating frequency increases, so X_L can be calculated according to:

$$X_L\,(\Omega) = 2 \cdot \pi \cdot f \cdot L$$

where f is the operating frequency and L is the inductance of the PL259/SO239 connection.

Referring to Figure 66, the SWR can be now be calculated where first coaxial cable is connected to the PL259/SO239 connectors at Point A as shown. The SWR is calculated using the reflection coefficient (ρ) Equation 15 and the SWR Equation 18, as described in Chapter 3:

$$\rho = \left| \frac{Z_L - Zo}{Z_L + Zo} \right|$$

or

$$\rho = \left| \frac{(50\Omega + jX_L) - 50\Omega}{(50\Omega + jX_L) + 50\Omega} \right| \tag{15}$$

where the vertical lines denote the modulus of ρ. Then:

$$SWR = \frac{1 + \rho}{1 - \rho} \tag{18}$$

The theoretical SWR was calculated at 10, 32, 100, 145, 230 and 432MHz with the results shown in **Table 5** and plotted as **Figure 67**. Referring to Figure 67, it can be seen that the theoretical SWR remains low up to 100MHz. However, the theoretical SWR at 200MHz is about 1.2:1, then continues to rise and is 1.45:1 at 432MHz. This indicates the increasing effect of the PL259/SO239 connection's inductive reactance (X_L) as the frequency is increased.

The theoretical results between 10 and 432MHz provided a basis for a comparison with the measurements to be described, which were made using actual

Frequency (MHz)	PL259/SO259 coupling input impedance (Ω)	SWR seen at PL259/SO239 connection with first coaxial cable (Point A)
10	+j 0.40	1:1
32	+j 1.27	1:1
100	+j 4.00	1.1:1
145	+j 5.82	1.1:1
230	+j 9.36	1.2:1
432	+j 18.72	1.45:1

Table 5: Calculated results for the theoretical 50Ω coaxial cables connected using PL259 and SO239 connectors.

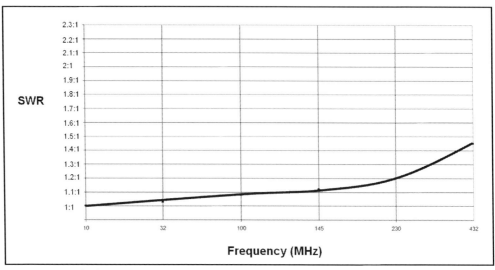

Figure 67: Calculated theoretical SWR at Point A against frequency for the 50Ω cables and PL259/SO239 connection represented in Figure 66.

cables terminated with PL259 plugs and connected using an SO239 coupling.

7.4.2. Measurements with actual coaxial cables

To assess the impact of using PL259 and SO239 connectors with actual 50Ω coaxial cables, a series of SWR measurements were made using an MFJ-269c antenna analyser as follows.

A) Calibration test run

The SWR was measured at the input of a 6m length of 50Ω coaxial cable terminated in PL259 plugs with its far end connected to a 50Ω dummy load. The measurements were made from 10MHz to 432MHz and then repeated with the coaxial cable connected the opposite way around. These tests provided a calibration run to check the consistency of the SWR measured. The results obtained for both directions were the same and are plotted as **Figure 68**.

B) Measurements with two 50Ω coaxial cables connected using PL259 and SO239 connectors

The 6m length of coaxial cable used for the calibration measurements was divided to form two cables of 4m and 2m in length, both terminated in PL259 plugs. The cables were connected using a SO239 coupling and then the SWR was measured in both directions, over the same frequency range. The SWR results obtained for both directions are also shown plotted in Figure 68.

Comparing the single cable calibration test with the 2m-connector-4m cable (2m-to-4m) and the 4m-connector-2m cable (4m-to-2m) tests in Figure 68, the curves follow the same general form up until around 200MHz. Above 200MHz, the 2m-to-4m and 4m-to-2m cable tests show the SWR worsening as the fre-

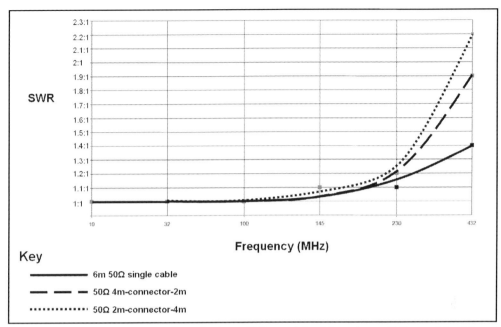

Figure 68: SWR measurement for a 6m long 50Ω coaxial cable and two 50Ω coaxial cables of length 4m and 2m connected using PL259 and SO239 connectors.

quency increases.

The worst case SWR was 2.2:1 at 432MHz, where the measurement was made into 2m long 50Ω coaxial cable which was then connected to the 4m long 50Ω coaxial cable using PL259/SO239 connectors (ie 2m-to-4m cable). However, when this cable combination was measured in the reverse direction (ie 4m-to-2m cable), the SWR lowered to 1.9:1 at 432MHz. These measurements provide an indication of masking effect introduced by the cables on the SWR observed (as described in Chapter 3). The masking effect of the coaxial cable can be seen from Figure 68, with the SWR worse when measured at the input to the shorter 2m length of coaxial cable as expected. However, both sets of results show the SWR rising above 100MHz and becoming significant at 432MHz with an SWR of about 2.1:1.

Compared to the theoretical SWR curve for a PL259/SO239 connection (shown in Figure 67), the measured SWR curves for a PL259/SO239 were close to the theoretical curve until 100MHz, when the SWR started to rise. However, at 432MHz the measured SWRs were much worse compared to the theoretically calculated SWR.

C) Comparison tests using N-type connectors

As a comparison, a series of tests were made using 50Ω coaxial cables connected using N-type connectors. A single 50Ω coaxial cable calibration test was made in both directions, using a cable with a length of 6m. Then a test using

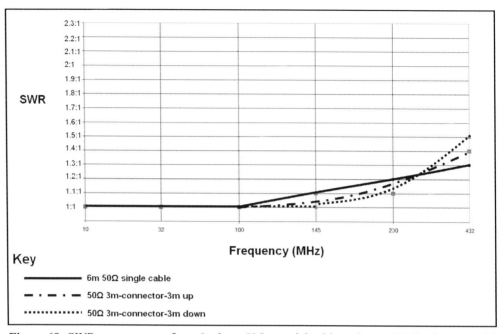

Figure 69: SWR measurement for a 6m long 50Ω coaxial cable and two 50Ω 3m long coaxial cables connected using N-type connectors.

two 50Ω coaxial cables connected using N-type connectors was made, where each cable had a length of 3m. The SWR results obtained from these tests are plotted in **Figure 69**. The worst case SWR measured was 1.5:1 at 432MHz for the two 50Ω coaxial cables connected using N-type connectors.

The SWR results for the N-type connected coaxial cables shown in Figure 69 are similar to those plotted in Figure 68 for the PL259/SO239 connection up to about 200MHz. However, above 200MHz, there is a significant improvement in the SWR measured for the N-type connected cables compared to the PL259/SO239 connection, with the SWR at 432MHz indicating that PL259 and SO239 connectors had become much be less effective.

This result is to be expected because N-type connectors tend to use air as the insulation between the plug and socket and the dimensions for R_s and r_c are chosen to try and maintain 50Ω through the connection, meaning less attenuation as the frequency increases.

7.4.3 Observations on the SWR tests and theoretical calculations made
Based on the SWR measurements and calculations made, PL259 and SO239 connectors provide a convenient means to connect 50Ω coaxial cables to radio equipment for frequencies up to about 200MHz. However, when using these connectors above 200MHz, the SWR tended to become high favouring the use of other types of connector with improved characteristics at these frequencies.

Using a Smith Chart

The Smith Chart provides a pictorial representation of a mismatched transmission line in terms of the impedances which are encountered as its length changes. To do this, the chart uses impedances described using Cartesian co-ordinates (R + jX) which are mapped onto a circular axis. This circular technique has the advantage over using a conventional straight-lined graph (eg Argand diagram) because it is suited to assessing the repetitive character of a standing wave along a mismatched transmission line. The Smith Chart also provides a very convenient method to quickly determine the standing wave ratio (SWR) for a mismatched transmission line [31].

8.1 Expressing an Impedance using Cartesian Co-ordinates

Impedance (Z) is a measure of the opposition to the flow of a current through a component when a voltage is applied across it. An impedance comprises a resistive and reactive part which can be expressed as:

$$Z \, (\Omega) = R + jX$$

By convention, the '+j' indicates an inductive reactance and a '-j' indicates a capacitive reactance [32] [33].

For example, an impedance having a resistance of 75Ω and an inductive reactance of 50Ω is conventionally written as:

$$Z = (75 + j50)\Omega$$

while an impedance having a resistance of 33Ω and a capacitive reactance of 38Ω is conventionally written as:

$$Z = (33 - j38)\Omega$$

In terms of the relationship between the total current (I) flowing through a component and a voltage (V) applied across the component this is given by:

$$I(amps) = \frac{V(volts)}{Z(\Omega)}$$

Impedance can be represented by plotting its resistive and reactive parts on a chart called an Argand diagram using a Cartesian co-ordinate system as shown in **Figure 70**. The central horizontal axis represents the impedance's resistance (termed the *real* part) while the vertical axis represents the reactance (termed the *imaginary* part).

The Argand diagram can be used to plot a series of measurements at various frequencies, which produces an impedance signature for the component. However, when the impedance measurements are for a transmission line, analysing the impedances at specific points along the transmission line can become difficult to perform using an Argand diagram. This arises because of

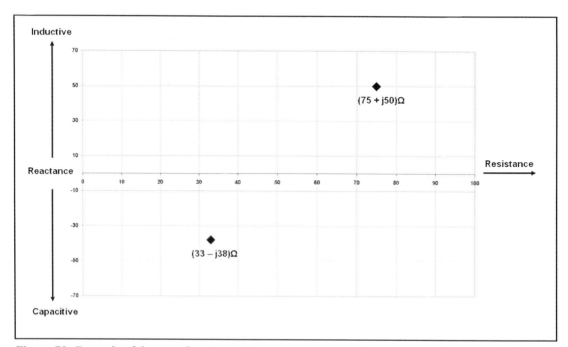

Figure 70: Example of the use of an Argand diagram to plot inductive and capacitive impedances (Z) of (33 − j33)Ω and (75 + j50)Ω respectively.

the cyclic nature of the impedances as they occur along the transmission line. Therefore, to make it easier when analysing the impedances encountered with transmission lines, a Smith Chart provides a suitable pictorial approach to visualise how the impedance along the transmission line changes depending upon the line's length [34] [35].

8.2 The Smith Chart

The Smith Chart is a pictorial representation of a transmission line in terms of the impedances which are encountered travelling along the line. The chart uses impedances described using Cartesian co-ordinates mapped on to a circular axis. For mismatched lines, the Smith Chart provides a convenient way to determine the standing wave ratio (SWR) and changes in the impedance at points along a transmission line's length.

A typical Smith Chart, used to determine impedance transformations along a transmission line, is shown in **Figure 71** [36] where the co-ordinate lines are sec-

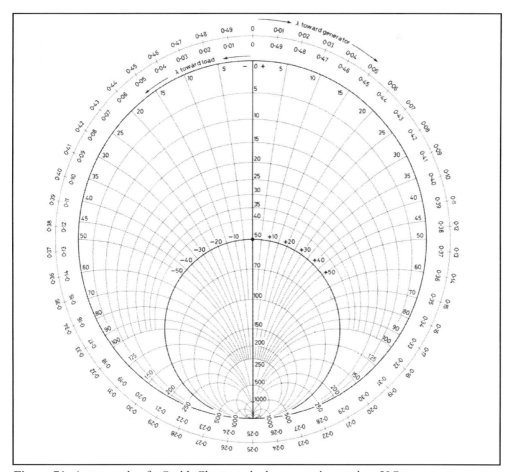

Figure 71: An example of a Smith Chart used when assessing against 50Ω.

tions of a circle rather than being straight lines. By convention, the Smith Chart has a straight resistance (R) scale which decreases towards zero as shown. The curved lines, which fan out either side of the resistive scale, represent the reactance with inductance reactance shown (in this case) to the right (+jX) and capacitance reactance to the left (-jX).

Some readers may find it easier to read the Smith Chart with resistive scale running horizontally, while others may prefer to use the Smith Chart with this scale running vertically. Therefore, to use the chart, it may be easier to orientate the book as is felt appropriate or comfortable.

The scale running around the circumference of the chart allows the transmission line to be assessed in terms of its electrical wavelength. Moving halfway around the chart equals travelling a quarter wavelength (λ/4) along the transmission line, while a full rotation equals a half wavelength (λ/2). This scale comprises two sub-scales allowing the directions towards the 'generator' or 'load' to be assessed. The point at the centre of the Smith Chart is known as the chart's prime centre and in Figure 71 this is 50Ω.

8.3 Using a Smith Chart

When the terminating load impedance (Z_L) does not equal the transmission line's characteristic impedance (Zo), the line is said to be mismatched. This has the effect that the load's impedance is changed by the line's transforming effect along the line's length. These changes are found from an SWR circle plotted on the Smith Chart centred on the chart's 50Ω prime centre and passing through where the load impedance is plotted.

Example 1: Constructing an SWR circle
In this example, a coaxial cable with a characteristic impedance (Zo) of 50Ω is terminated by an antenna having a purely resistive load (Z_L) of 25Ω. This can be represented as a complex impedance of (25 + j0)Ω and is shown plotted as Point A on the Smith Chart in **Figure 72**. An SWR circle is then drawn which passes through this point whose radius is located on the chart's prime centre (ie at the centre). In this case, this circle represents an SWR of 2:1 and is shown as the black thicker line circle in Figure 72. Any point on the chart crossed by this circle represents an impedance giving the same mismatch condition. For example, the circle also passes through (100 + j0)Ω, shown as Point B, located directly opposite Point A and this will also result in an SWR of 2:1.

Mathematically, the SWR could be calculated using Equation 18, as described in Chapter 3:

$$SWR = \frac{1 + |\rho|}{1 - |\rho|}$$

(18)

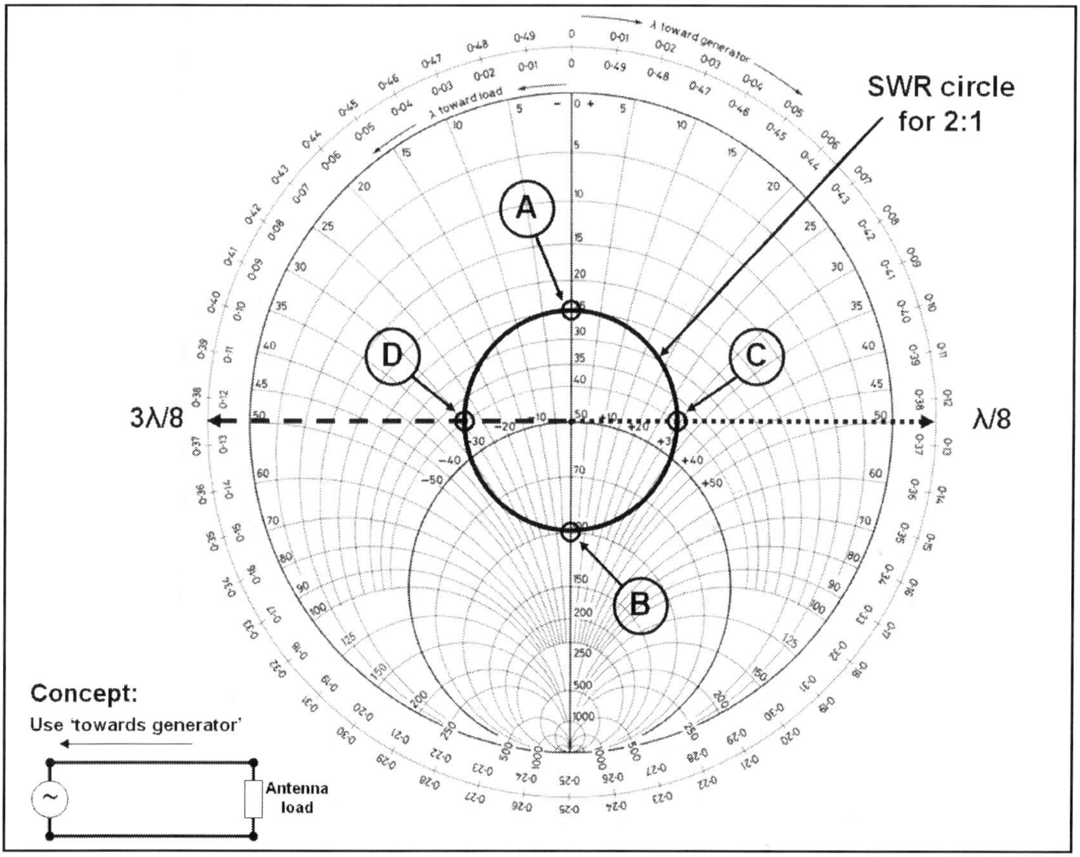

Figure 72: Examples 1 and 2. Plotting an SWR circle and moving around the Smith Chart.

where ρ is the reflection coefficient given by Equation 15, also described in Chapter 3:

$$|\rho| = \left| \frac{Z_L - Zo}{Z_L + Zo} \right|$$

(15)

The vertical lines either side of the quantities shown in Equations 15 and 18 show that the modulus values need to be used in the calculation (ie not complex values). However, in this example, Zo and Z_L are pure resistances of 50Ω and 25Ω respectively which simplifies the calculation. Therefore:

$$|\rho| = \left| \frac{(25\Omega - 50\Omega)}{(25\Omega + 50\Omega)} \right| = 0.3333$$

(to four decimal places)

Then using Equation (18), the SWR is:

$$SWR = \frac{(1+0.3333)}{(1-0.3333)} = 2$$

(ie an SWR of 2:1).

Consequently, this load has given rise to an SWR of 2:1. However, another impedance could give a different SWR which would be represented by another SWR circle which passes through where this impedance is plotted on the chart, also centred on the chart's prime centre. For example if Z_L was 12.5Ω, then rerunning the calculation above gives an SWR of 4:1 and this would give an SWR circle which runs through 12.5Ω and 200Ω on the resistance scale.

Example 2: Moving along the transmission line

Using Figure 72 and the same antenna load (Z_L) as above (ie (25 + j0)Ω), the load's termination to the coaxial cable can be thought of as starting where the resistive scale crosses the outer circular electrical wavelength scale (ie where this circular scale shows 0). Moving clockwise away from the position of the load towards the end of the coaxial cable (ie 'towards the generator'), if a line is taken from the chart's 50Ω prime centre towards the electrical wavelength scale, then this enables the impedance to be found where this line intersects with the SWR circle. For example, where the line intersects at λ/8 'towards the generator' (black dotted arrow), this crosses the SWR circle where the imped-ance is (40 + j30)Ω (ie Point C). If the coaxial cable was to be cut at Point C, with Z_L still equal to 25Ω, then measuring the impedance (Z) at Point C should give (40 + j30)Ω.

Moving on to λ/4 gives a measured impedance of (100 + j0)Ω at Point B. Then continuing on to 3λ/8 gives an impedance of (40 - j30)Ω at Point D (black dashed arrow). Points C and D have been shown on Figure 72 for reference.

Effectively, the Smith Chart provides a pictorial indication of the impedance along the transmission line at a specific point, on the SWR circle, away from where the impedance Z_L terminates the line. This illustrates how a mismatched transmission line has a transforming effect upon the impedance Z_L terminating it.

The example above was based on using a coaxial cable, however the same result would have been obtained for a twin-line cable having the same characteristic impedance (Zo) as the coaxial cable.

Example 3: Finding an antenna's impedance from the measured imped-ance at the end of the transmission line

When an antenna is connected to one end of a coaxial cable, then its impedance can be found using an impedance measurement made at the other end of the coaxial cable. However, the cable's electrical length must be known to do this.

In this example, the measured impedance was (25 + j40)Ω and the cable's

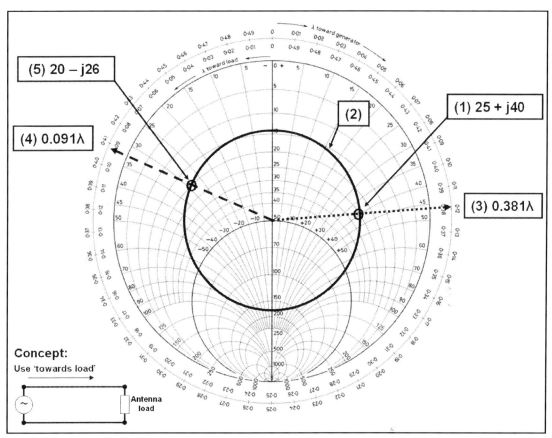

Figure 73: Example 3. Finding an antenna's impedance from a measured impedance at the end of the transmission line.

electrical length was 0.21 wavelengths. Referring to **Figure 73**:

- Plot the measured impedance of (25 + j40)Ω on the Smith Chart and shown as (1).

- Draw the SWR circle passing through this point whose radius is centred on the chart's prime centre (2).

- From the chart's prime centre, extend a line out passing through the plotted point to intersect with the scale marked 'wavelengths towards load'. This is shown as the dotted black arrow.

Make a note of the number where the line crosses, this should be 0.381 wavelengths (3).

Add the electrical length of coaxial cable to this number:

0.381 + 0.21 = 0.591 wavelengths

0.591 wavelengths is off the Smith Chart's scale because it is too long. So, to compensate for this, subtract 0.5, giving 0.091 wavelengths.

- Extend a second line from the chart's prime centre to intersect with 0.091 on the chart's '*wavelengths towards load*' scale (4). This is shown as dashed black arrow.

- The antenna's impedance can be found where the second line crosses the SWR circle. In this case this is close to **(20 – j26)Ω** (5).

Example 4: Measuring a coaxial cable's electrical length

As described in Example 3, when an antenna (or other load) is connected to one end of a coaxial cable, then its impedance can be found by making a measurement at the other end of the cable. However, to do this, the cable's electrical length must be known and this example describes how this may be done.

A technique to determine the electrical length of a feeder cable is to use a RF impedance measurement set and a Smith Chart. However, this technique assumes that the feeder cable's losses are low. In the following example, the measured impedance was (100 + j40)Ω. Using the Smith Chart shown in

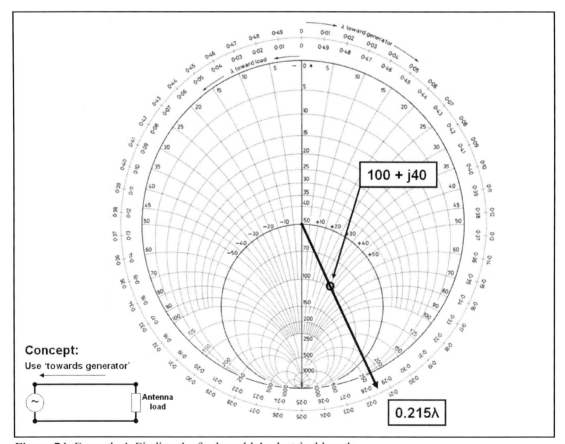

Figure 74: Example 4. Finding the feeder cable's electrical length.

Figure 74, the technique is summarised as follows:

- Terminate the end of the coaxial cable with a 22Ω resistor.

- Measure the impedance at the other end of the coaxial cable. In this case this was (100 + j40)Ω.

- Plot the measured impedance of (100 + j40)Ω on the Smith Chart.

- Extend a line from the chart's prime centre though (100 + j40)Ω to intersect with the '*electrical wavelength towards generator*' scale as shown.

- Where the line intersects with the '*electrical wavelength towards generator*' scale, this gives the coaxial cable's electrical length. In this example, this is **0.215** electrical wavelengths (ie 0.21λ).

The electrical length of the cable may be several and a part half wavelengths long. The Smith Chart will only register the part of the half electrical wavelength which is applicable to the impedance transforming effect.

8.4 The normalised Smith Chart

The use of the Smith Chart described so far is limited to calculations involving 50Ω transmission lines only. Using a normalised Smith Chart [36] allows calculations to be made referred to any impedance. If a 50Ω Smith Chart has its axes divided by 50, then the result is a normalised Smith Chart as shown in **Figure 75**. The Smith Chart's prime centre now becomes 1, the 25Ω grid-line is 0.5, the 100Ω grid-line is 2, the -30Ω grid-line is -0.6 and so on.

Example 5: Antenna impedance calculation using a normalised Smith Chart
Previously in Example 3, the antenna's impedance was found when (25 + j40)Ω was measured at the end of the 50Ω coaxial cable whose electrical length was 0.21 wavelengths. This example is re-calculated using a normalised Smith Chart and

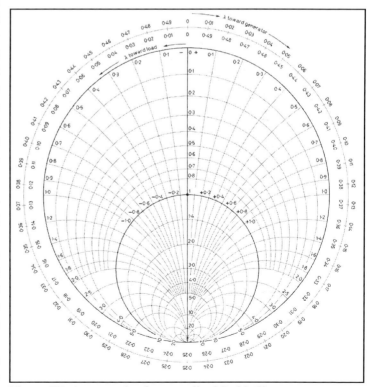

Figure 75: An example of a normalised Smith Chart.

109

shown as **Figure 76**:

- Divide the measured impedance of (25 + j40)Ω by 50 to give the normalised impedance:

  $Z_{normalised} = (0.5 + j0.8)$

- Plot the normalised impedance (0.5 + j0.8) on the Smith Chart (A) as shown in Figure 76.

- Draw the SWR circle passing through this point whose radius is located on the chart's prime centre (B).

- From the chart's prime centre extend a line out, which passes through the plotted point, to intersect with the scale marked '*wavelengths towards load*'. This intersection is at 0.381 electrical wavelengths (C). This is shown as the dotted black arrow in Figure 76.

- Add this intersection number to the electrical length of the cable (0.21 wavelengths):

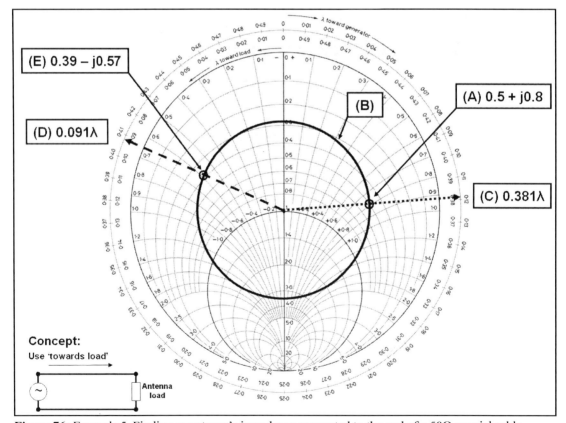

Figure 76: Example 5. Finding an antenna's impedance connected to the end of a 50Ω coaxial cable.

0.381 + 0.21 = 0.591 wavelengths.

- 0.591 wavelengths are off the Smith Chart's scale because it is too long. So, to compensate for this, subtract 0.5 giving 0.091 wavelengths.

- Extend a second line from the chart's prime centre to intersect with 0.091 on the Smith Chart's 'wavelengths towards load' scale (D). This is shown as the dashed black arrow in Figure 76.

- The antenna's normalised impedance is found where the second line crosses the SWR circle (E). In this case this is close to (0.39 – j0.57).

- Multiplying the normalised impedance by 50 gives the antenna's impedance of **(19.5 – j28.5)Ω**.

Note
In Example 3, the calculation using a 50Ω chart gave (20 – j29)Ω.

Example 6: A new antenna impedance calculation
In this example, which is shown in **Figure 77**, the impedance was measured at

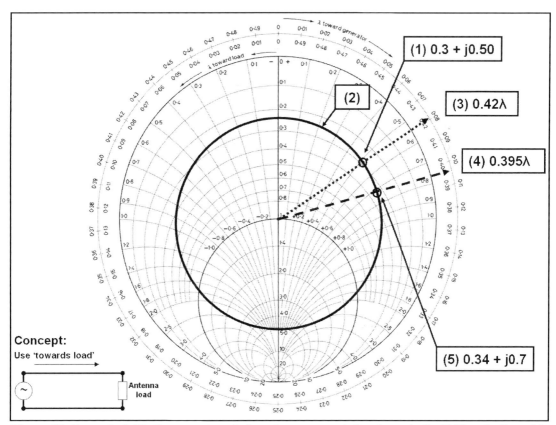

Figure 77: Example 6. Finding an antenna's impedance connected to the end of a 300Ω twin-line cable (ladder-line).

the end of a twin-line cable (ladder-line), whose characteristic impedance was 300Ω and an electrical length of 0.475 wavelengths. The measured impedance was (90+ j150)Ω at the end of a twin-line cable (ladder-line).

- Dividing (90 + j150)Ω by 300 gave a normalised impedance of:

- $Z_{normalised}$ = (0.3 + j0.5)

- Plot the normalised impedance (0.3 + j0.5) on the Smith Chart as shown in Figure 77 (1).

- Draw the SWR circle passing through this point whose radius is located on the chart's prime centre (2).

- From the chart's prime centre, extend a line outwards passing through the plotted point to intersect with the scale marked '*wavelengths towards load*'. This intersection is close to 0.42 wavelengths and is shown as the dotted black arrow in Figure 77 (3).

- Add this number to the electrical length of twin-line cable:

0.42 + 0.475 = 0.895 wavelengths

- 0.895 wavelengths are off the Smith Chart's scale. So, to compensate, subtract 0.5, giving 0.395 wavelengths.

- Extend a second line from the chart's prime centre to intersect with 0.395 on the chart's '*wavelengths towards load*' outer scale and is shown as the dashed black arrow in Figure 77 (4).

- The antenna's normalised impedance can be found where the second line crosses the SWR circle (5). In this case this is close to (0.34 + j0.7).

- Multiplying the normalised impedance by 300 gives the antenna's imped-ance of **(102 – j210)Ω**.

8.5 Examining impedance changes for a G5RV antenna

The examples to follow use a normalised Smith Chart to provide an indication of how the impedance of a G5RV antenna changes at the bottom of the balanced feeder cable as the band of operation is changed from 20m to 80m.

8.5.1 Background

The G5RV antenna has a wire span length of three half electrical wavelengths (3λ/2), fed at its centre by a balanced feeder cable of half an electrical wavelength (λ/2) long at the desired resonant frequency [37] [38].

A full-size G5RV antenna is often thought of as a wire span of 31.1m (102ft) long centrally fed using about 10.34m (34ft) of balanced feeder cable. This configuration of the antenna covers operation on the bands from 80m to 10m and is resonant on the 20m band.

In this example, the balanced feeder cable's characteristic impedance (Zo) was 450Ω (eg window-line).

Example 7: 20m operation

Using the MMANA-GAL antenna analysing application [39], the impedance was predicted for a G5RV antenna, at a frequency of 14.3MHz. The antenna's feed point impedance (at the wire span's centre) was predicted as 113Ω (resistive) when the wire span was installed at 12m AGL.

On the 20m band, the antenna's balanced feeder cable's length is close to half a wavelength. This has the effect that the impedance seen at the end of the balanced feeder cable is close to the antenna's feed point impedance (ie 113Ω in this case).

Example 8: 80m operation

At 3.575MHz, the antenna's feed point impedance was predicted using the same MMANA-GAL antenna model as (21 − j405)Ω with the wire span at 12m AGL. The length of the feeder cable is now close to 0.125 wavelengths on the 80m band. The impedance at the bottom of the balanced feeder cable can now be determined using a normalised Smith Chart as shown in **Figure 78**:

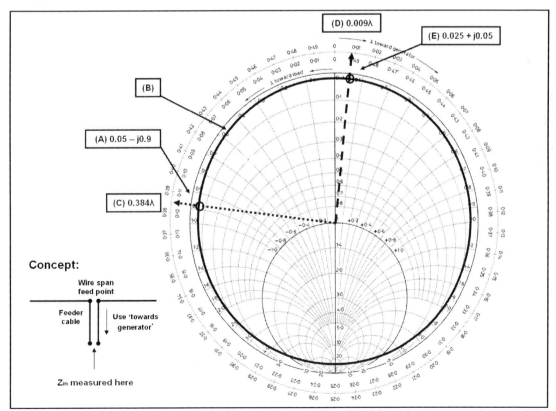

Figure 78: Example 8. Assessing how a G5RV antenna's normalised impedance seen at the end of the twin-line feeder cable has changed on the 80m band.

- Dividing $(21 - j405)\Omega$ by 450 (Zo in this case) gives a normalised imped-ance of:

$Z_{normalised} = (0.05 - j0.9)$

- The normalised impedance $(0.05 - j0.9)$ was plotted on the Smith Chart as shown in Figure 78 (A).

- The SWR circle was drawn passing through this point on the Smith Chart with its radius centred on the chart's prime centre (B).

- From the chart's prime centre, a line was extended outwards passing through the plotted point to intersect with the scale marked '*wavelengths towards generator*' This intersection is 0.384 wavelengths (C). This is shown as the dotted black arrow in Figure 78.

- Add this intersection number to the electrical length of cable:

$0.384 + 0.125 = 0.509$ wavelengths

- 0.509 wavelengths are off the Smith Chart's scale. So, to compensate, subtract 0.5, giving 0.009 wavelengths.

- Extend a second line outwards from the chart's prime centre to intersect with 0.009 on the chart's '*wavelengths towards generator*' scale (D). This is shown as the dashed black arrow in Figure 78.

- The antenna's normalised impedance is found where the second line crosses the SWR circle (E). In this case this was close to $(0.025 + j0.05)$.

- Multiplying the normalised impedance by 450 gives antenna's impedance of around **$(11.25 + j22.5)\Omega$**.

Note

The MMANA-GAL G5RV antenna model predicted impedance was $(13 + j22.25)\Omega$ as a comparison.

This example shows that the impedance of the G5RV antenna has changed at the bottom of the balanced feeder cable to around $(11.25 + j22.5)\Omega$ when operating on the 80m. As a comparison on the 20m band, the impedance at the bottom of the balanced feeder cable was 113Ω.

Example 9: 40m operation

The previous process used in Example 8 was repeated at 7.15MHz with the MMANA-GAL G5RV antenna model now predicting the antenna's feed point impedance as $(644 - j1230)\Omega$. The 450Ω feeder cable is now close to 0.25 wavelengths long on the 40m band.

- Dividing (644+ j1230)Ω by 450 gives:

  $Z_{normalised}$ = (1.43 + j2.73)

- The normalised impedance (1.43 + j2.73) was plotted on the Smith Chart as shown in **Figure 79** (1).

- The SWR circle was drawn passing through this point on the Smith Chart with its radius centred on the chart's prime centre (2).

- From the Smith Chart's prime centre, extend a line outwards passing through the plotted point to intersect with the scale marked '*wavelengths towards generator*'. This intersection is close to 0.2 wavelengths (3). This is shown as the dotted black arrow in Figure 79.

- Add this intersection number to the electrical length of cable:

  0.2 + 0.25 = 0.45 wavelengths

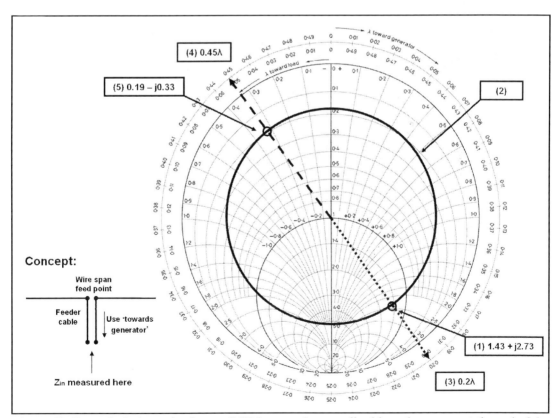

Figure 79: Example 9. Assessing how a G5RV antenna's normalised impedance seen at the end of the twin-line feeder cable has changed on the 40m band.

- Extend a second line from the chart's prime centre to intersect with 0.45 on the chart's *wavelengths towards generator* outer scale (4). This is shown as the dashed black arrow in Figure 79.

- The antenna's normalised impedance is found where the second line crosses the SWR circle (5). In this case this is close to (0.19 - j0.33).

- Multiplying the normalised impedance by 450 gives antenna's impedance around **(86 – j149)Ω**.

Note

The MMANA-GAL G5RV antenna model predicted impedance was (81.3 - j163.4)Ω as a comparison.

This example shows that the impedance of the G5RV antenna has changed at the bottom of the balanced feeder cable to around (86 – j149)Ω when operating on the 40m. As a comparison on the 20m band, the impedance at the bottom of the balanced feeder cable was 113Ω.

8.6 Converting an impedance to an admittance

To follow is an example of how to use a normalised Smith Chart to calculate an admittance from a known impedance. The reference impedance used in this example was 50Ω, however the technique is applicable to any other required reference impedance (eg 75Ω, 300Ω, 450Ω and so forth).

Example 10: Impedance to an Admittance conversion process

Earlier, the impedance below was used within Figure 70:

$$Z = (75 + j50)Ω$$

This impedance is used for this example.

- Convert the known impedance to a normalised impedance by dividing each of the impedance's components by the value the prime centre represents. In this case, the reference impedance is 50Ω giving:

$$Z_{normalised} = 1.5 + j1$$

- Plot this normalised impedance (1.5 + j1) on the Smith Chart as shown in **Figure 80** (A).

- Draw the SWR circle which passes through this point on the Smith Chart with its radius centred on the chart's prime centre (B).

- Extend a straight line across the Smith Chart which passes through its prime centre and through the plotted point as shown (C). This is shown as a dashed black line in Figure 80.

- Where the dashed line intersects with the SWR circle directly opposite the plotted normalised impedance (A) gives the normalised admittance (D). This is 0.46 - j0.32.

- This figure is converted to the actual admittance (in siemens) by dividing it by 50. This is **(0.0092 - j0.0064)**.

Rerunning this example using the second impedance from Figure 70 of:

$$Z = (33 - j38)\Omega$$

This impedance gives an admittance of **(0.01 + j0.02)** using the technique described above when referred to 50Ω.

By mathematical calculation, $(75 + j50)^{-1}$ gives a result of 0.0092 - j0.0062, while $(33 + j38)^{-1}$ gives a result of 0.013 + j0.015. These results show that the normalised Smith Chart provides a practical solution to determining an admittance from an impedance.

8.7 Observations when using a Smith Chart

The aim of the examples used within this chapter has been to provide a practical guide to using a Smith Chart. As with many graphical techniques, the Smith Chart has its benefits and constraints.

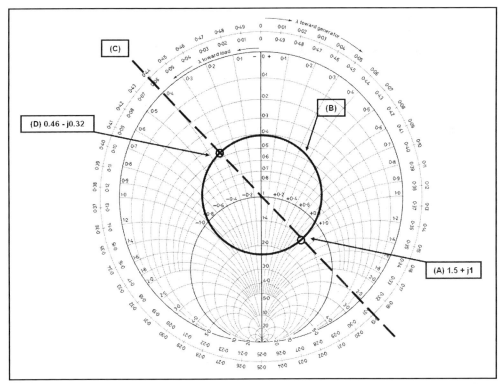

Figure 80: Example 10. Impedance to an Admittance conversion process using a normalised Smith Chart.

Benefits include:

- The Smith Chart avoids manipulating equations involving complex number theory to determine a final outcome.

- The Smith Chart provides a pictorial representation of the impedances encountered along a mismatched transmission line, which can be easier to understand and visualise compared to working with line equations.

- Once understood, the Smith Chart becomes relatively straightforward to use.

Constraints include:

- Care is needed when plotting and extracting information using the Smith Chart, otherwise errors can occur in the results obtained.

- When determining the electrical length of a transmission line, it is only the last part half electrical wavelength that can be found and not the whole line's length.

- No account is taken of a transmission line's loss when using a Smith Chart.

- The user requires an understanding of how to handle imaginary numbers.

ADMITTANCE

The method of calculating the total value of several resistors in series is to add their individual values. A straightforward way of calculating the total value when several resistors are in parallel is to add their reciprocals. The answer obtained will also be a reciprocal and has to be converted back to a resistance (R), by dividing 1 by the answer:

$$1/R1 + 1/R2 + 1/R3 = 1/Rt \text{ and the total resistance } Rt = 1 / (1/Rt).$$

The reciprocal of R is conductance (symbol G) and working using G simplifies calculations when several resistors are connected in parallel. Each individual conductance (ie G1, G2, G3 and so on) are added together to give a final value (Gt), the reciprocal of Gt gives the total resistance (R) in Ω. The reciprocal (or the dual) of impedance is admittance (symbol Y) and reciprocal of reactance is susceptance (symbol B). The unit of conductance, susceptance and admittance is the siemen (S).

When making measurements, it is important to be aware of the RF impedance measurement set's selected setting. If the RF impedance measurement set is switched to measure admittance (Y) then the result, like the calculation of parallel resistors described above, will need to be converted into the more familiar ohms to give an impedance.

Annex 1:
The Propagation Constant

The propagation constant (γ) describes the logarithmic rate of decay of a signal waveform in terms of how it has travelled down a transmission line. Therefore, the propagation constant (γ) relates to both the transmission line's loss and to the phase-change of a wave travelling down the line.

The propagation constant (γ) comprises a real term and an imaginary term (denoted by j). The real term gives the attenuation coefficient (α), while the imaginary term gives the phase-change coefficient (β) as described in Chapter 2. Hence, there is a relationship between γ, α and β such that:

Propagation constant $(\gamma) = \alpha + j\beta$

where the attenuation coefficient (α) is in nepers per metre and the phase-change coefficient (β) is the number of degrees, or radians, phase lag per metre.

The derivation of the propagation constant (γ) involves the transmission line's primary coefficients of its loop resistance (R), loop inductance (L), parallel capacitance (C) and parallel conductance (G) which were described in Chapter 2. The derivation of a transmission line's propagation constant (γ) can be found in references [4] and [40], with an explanation of the wave equation used found in reference [41].

If the primary line coefficients for a transmission are known, then the line's propagation constant (γ) can be calculated to find the attenuation coefficient (α) and the phase-change coefficient (β). Two examples follow where the propagation constant (γ) has been calculated in terms of its α and β components, including the relevant complex number theory. The first example uses a low operating frequency (f), while the second example uses a much higher frequency to demonstrate the effect on the transmission line's performance as the operating frequency is increased.

Example A1.1 [42]

A twin-cable has the following primary line coefficients:

Loop resistance	(R):	30Ω/km
Conductance	(G):	1µS/km
Loop inductance	(L):	1mH/km
Capacitance	(C):	0.2µF/km

Before using this cable to carry a signal, the cable's impedance (Zo), attenuation coefficient (α), phase-change coefficient (β) and attenuation (dB) need to be calculated over a length of 15km. The angular velocity of the signal to be carried by the cable is 5000 radians/second.

Note 1:

5000 radians/s = $2 \times \pi \times f$ where f is the frequency

The characteristic impedance (Zo):

For a kilometre (km) long section of line, Equation 2 allows Zo to be calculated:

$$Zo\ (\Omega) = \sqrt{\frac{(R + j2 \cdot \pi \cdot f \cdot L)}{(G + j2 \cdot \pi \cdot f \cdot C)}}$$

(2)

$(R + j2 \cdot \pi \cdot f \cdot L) = 30 + j(5000 \times 1mH) \qquad = 30 + j5$

$(G + j2 \cdot \pi \cdot f \cdot C) = 1 \times 10^{-6} + j(5000 \times 0.2\mu F) = (1 + j1000) \times 10^{-6}$

To ease calculations, the complex numbers above have been expressed in their polar format:

$30 + j5 \qquad = 30.41 \ \underline{|9.46°}$

$(1 + j1000) \times 10^{-6} = 1000 \times 10^{-6} \ \underline{|89.94°}$

Note 2

The polar form for a complex number uses its modulus referred to the angle (θ) between the complex number's real (R) and imaginary (X) components.

Note 3
The modulus is given by

$$\sqrt{X^2 + R^2}$$

Note 4
The angle between the real (R) and imaginary components (X) is given by

$$\tan^{-1}(X/R)$$

Note 5
When the numerator or denominator are comparatively small numbers, best practice is to work the calculations to two, or more, decimal places to improve the accuracy of the results.

Therefore:

$$|Zo| = \sqrt{\frac{30.41}{1000 \times 10^{-6}}} \qquad = 174.38\Omega$$

$$Zo \text{ Angle } \theta = \frac{(9.46 - 89.94°)}{2} = -40.24°$$

The cable's characteristic impedance

$$(Zo) = 174.38 \ \underline{|-40.24°} \text{ ohms}(\Omega)$$

The propagation constant (γ)
For a one kilometre (km) long section of line, Equation 14 allows γ to be calculated:

$$\text{Propagation constant } (\gamma) = \sqrt{(R + j2 \cdot \pi \cdot f \cdot L) \times (G + j2 \cdot \pi \cdot f \cdot C)} \quad (14)$$

Therefore (and from the above):

$$\text{Propagation constant } (\gamma) = \sqrt{(30.41 \ \underline{|9.46°}) \times (1000 \times 10^{-6} \ \underline{|89.94°})}$$

Thus:

$$|\gamma| = \sqrt{(30.41)\times(1000 \times 10^{-6})} = 0.1744$$

$$\text{Angle } \theta = \frac{(9.46° + 89.94°)}{2} = 49.7°$$

The cable's propagation constant

$$(\gamma) = 0.1744 \underline{|49.7°} \text{ radians/km}$$

Using the above:

Attenuation coefficient (α) = 0.1744 × cosine $(49.7°)$ = 0.1128 nepers/km

Phase-change coefficient (β) = 0.1744 × sine $(49.7°)$ = 0.133 radians/km

The attenuation over a 15km length of the cable is:

Attenuation = 0.1128 nepers/km × 15km = 1.692 nepers

This loss represents a current, or voltage, ratio of 5.43:1.

Therefore, the loss over 15km of line in dB is 20 × log (5.43) =14.696dB

Example A1.2

A 900 telephony channel frequency division multiplex (FDM) system operates over a frequency from 312kHz to 4.028MHz [43]. The FDM system connects two telephone exchanges over a coaxial cable, whose primary line coefficients are shown below:

Loop resistance	(R):	17.06Ω/km
Conductance	(G):	0.002µS/km
Loop inductance	(L):	0.37mH/km
Capacitance	(C):	65.62nF/km

To verify the performance of the coaxial cable at 4.028MHz, a series of measurements were made. However, before these could be done, the coaxial cable's characteristic impedance (Zo) and propagation constant (γ) needed to be calculated.

The characteristic impedance (Zo)

For a kilometre (km) long section of line, Equation 2 allows Zo to be calculated:

$$Zo\ (\Omega) = \sqrt{\frac{(R + j2 \cdot \pi \cdot f \cdot L)}{(G + j2 \cdot \pi \cdot f \cdot C)}}$$

(2)

$$(R + j2 \cdot \pi \cdot f \cdot L) = 17.06 \times j(2 \times \pi \times 4.028\text{MHz} \times 0.37\text{mH}) = 17.06 + j9364.21$$

$$(G + j2 \cdot \pi \cdot f \cdot C) = 2 \times 10^{-9} + j(2 \times \pi \times 4.028\text{MHz} \times 65.62\text{nf}) = 2 \times 10^{-9} + j1.661$$

The value for G is extremely small and so its effect becomes negligible within the calculations to follow.

To ease calculations, the complex numbers above have been expressed in their polar format:

$$17.06 + j9364.21 \quad = 9364.22 \; \underline{|89.896°}$$

$$2 \times 10^{-9} + j1.661 \quad = \quad 1.661 \; \underline{|90°}$$

Therefore, and using Notes 2 to 5 above:

$$|Zo| = \sqrt{\frac{9364.22}{1.661}} = 75 \,\text{ohms}\,(\Omega)$$

$$Zo \text{ Angle } \theta = \frac{(89.896° - 90°)}{2} = -(0.052°)$$

The coaxial cable's characteristic impedance

$$(Zo) = 75 \; \underline{|-0.052°} \; \text{ohms}\,(\Omega)$$

Angle θ is extremely small, therefore Zo = 75Ω.

The propagation constant (γ)

For a one kilometre (km) long section of line, Equation 14 allows γ to be cal-culated:

$$\text{Propagation constant } (\gamma) \; = \; \sqrt{(R + j2 \cdot \pi \cdot f \cdot L) \times (G + j2 \cdot \pi \cdot f \cdot C)} \quad (14)$$

Therefore (and from the above):

$$\text{Propagation constant} (\gamma) = \sqrt{(936.22 \; \underline{|89.896°}) \times (1.661 \underline{|90°})}$$

Thus:

$$|\gamma| = \sqrt{9364.22 \times 1.661} = 124.72$$

$$\text{Angle } \theta \; = \; \frac{(89.896° + 90°)}{2} \; = \; 89.948°$$

The coax cable's propagation constant

$$(\gamma) = 124.72 \; \underline{|89.948°} \text{ radians/km}$$

Using the above:

$$\text{Attenuation coefficient} (\alpha) = 124.72 \text{ x cosine } (89.948°) = 0.113 \text{ nepers/km}$$

$$\text{Phase-change coefficient} (\beta) = 124.72 \text{ x sine} (89.948°) = 124.72 \text{ radians/km}$$

Often wideband repeater stations were placed at 1.85km intervals, along the transmission line between the telephone exchanges, to amplify the FDM signal being transmitted. Therefore, at 1.85km from the first telephone exchange:

Attenuation (α)

The attenuation

$$= \alpha \times 1.85 = 0.209 \text{ nepers}$$

representing a current, or voltage, ratio of 1.23:1.

Therefore, the loss of 1.85km of line in dB is

$$20 \times \log (1.226) = 1.82\text{dB}$$

Phase change (β)

The phase change (β) over 1.85km is given by:

$$\beta \times 1.85 = 124.72 \times 1.85 = 230.73 \text{ radians}$$

RF Signal's Wavelength (λ_{Line}) within the transmission line

Using the phase change (β) calculated above, the number of wavelengths (λ_{Line}) contained within the coaxial cable is given by:

$$\text{Number of wavelengths} = (230.73 / (2 \times \pi)) = 36.72$$

Therefore,

$$\lambda_{Line} = 1850\text{m} / 36.72 = 50.38\text{m}$$

Velocity factor (V_p)

The velocity factor (V_p) of the coaxial cable can be found from the RF signal's free space wavelength (λ) and its wavelength within the transmission line (λ_{line}).

At 4.028MHz, the free space wavelength (λ) is given by:

$$\text{Free space wavelength} (\lambda) = (300 / 4.028) = 74.47\text{m}$$

From the above

$$\lambda_{line} = 50.38m$$

Therefore:

$$\text{Velocity factor}\left(V_p\right) = \left(\lambda_{Line}/\lambda\right) = \left(50.38m \ / \ 74.47m\right) = 0.677$$

The velocity of propagation (V_p) can also be determined from the coaxial cable's primary coefficients of L and C using Equation 13 (where L and C are quoted per metre rather than per km):

$$V_p = \frac{1}{\sqrt{L \cdot C}} = \frac{1}{\sqrt{(0.37\mu H \times 65.62pF)}} = 2.0295 \times 10^8 m/s \tag{13}$$

Velocity factor is given by dividing V_p by the speed of light (3×10^8 m/s):

$$\text{Calculated velocity factor} = \left(2.0295 \times 10^8 / 3 \times 10^8\right) = 0.677$$

Annex 2:
The Maximum Power
Transfer Theorem

In electrical engineering, the maximum power transfer theorem states that the maximum electrical power is transferred from the source to the load when the internal resistance of the source equals the resistance of the load [44].

The transfer of electrical power from the source to its terminating load can be explained by using a load whose resistance can be varied. This concept is shown in **Figure 81**, where the power source is represented by a generator which has an internal resistance of Ri. In the power source's circuit, its generator is considered to be responsible for producing a constant voltage Vg and the power source's output is produced between Points A and B. The power source,

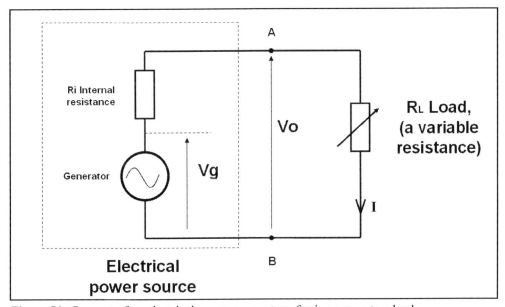

Figure 81: Concept of an electrical power source transferring power to a load.

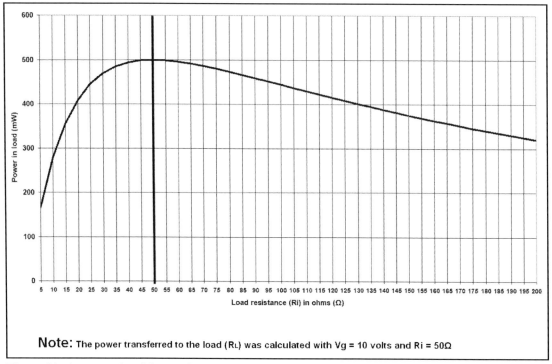

Figure 82: An example of the maximum power transfer theorem, when Ri and RL allows the maximum power to be transferred to the load (50Ω in this example).

comprising the generator and the series connected resistor Ri, effectively forms a Thevenin circuit in this context [44].

When no load is connected across the power source's output terminals A and B, then the output voltage Vo will equal Vg. However, when a load RL is connected across A and B then this allows a current I to flow. The voltage across the RL will be Vo, however its value will be determined by the potential divider formed by Ri and RL, where:

$$Vo(volts) = \left(\frac{R_L}{R_L + Ri}\right) \times Vg$$

The current (I) flowing is given by:

$$I(amps) = \frac{Vg}{R_L + Ri}$$

Taking Vo and I as their RMS values, the electrical power transferred to the load R_L is given by:

Power transferred (watts) = Vo x I

As the value of R_L is varied, so Vo and I will alter. Consequently, the electrical power transferred to the load R_L will also vary.

If the value of Vo is calculated for a number of values of R_L (ie the load), along with the corresponding value of I, then it is possible to determine how the power is transferred to the load as its resistance R_L is varied and this is shown as **Figure 82**.

In this example, the power source has an internal resistance Ri which has a value of 50Ω. From Figure 82, it can be seen that the maximum power is transferred from the power source to the load when R_L is also 50Ω. That is:

Maximum power transfer occurs when Ri = R$_L$

In Figure 82, this condition has been highlighted using the thicker vertical line running from the lower axis where 50Ω is denoted. When resistance R_L is equal to resistance Ri, then the two are said to be *matched*. If resistance R_L is not equal to resistance Ri, then the two are said to be *mismatched*.

If a transmission line could be made infinitely long, then if a voltage (V_{in}) is applied to the line's input it follows that this will cause a current (i) to flow (as previously shown in Figure 4). The characteristic impedance (Zo) of this infinitely long transmission line is then given by:

$$Zo(\Omega) = \frac{V_{in}}{i}$$

If this line is cut somewhere along its length and terminated with a load with an impedance which is equal to Zo, then the transmission line will continue to behave as if it were still infinitely long. When the load's impedance equals Zo, this situation is described as being *matched*. However, if the transmission line was terminated by a load with an impedance which is not equal to Zo, then not all the power will now be transferred to the load and there will be a *mismatch*. The power not absorbed by the load is reflected back down the line (referred to as the *reflected wave*) and this will cause a standing wave to be established along the transmission line as described in Chapter 3.

Therefore, to maintain the maximum transfer of power to the load from a transmission line, the load's impedance (Z_L) should equal the characteristic impedance (Zo) of the transmission line. For this reason the operation of a transmission line can be considered as being related to maximum power transfer theorem.

Annex 3:
Resistance values
for attenuators

In Chapter 3, Figures 18(a) and 18(b) illustrated the details for a 3dB and a 6dB theoretical attenuator for a 50Ω system. Table A3.1 summarises the details for theoretical attenuators from 1dB to 40dB in terms of three resistors R1, R2 and R3 that form a T-network as shown in **Figure 83**, which is suitable for use with coaxial cable systems [45].

The power dissipated by each resistor should be calculated before making up an attenuator based on the RF power to be supplied by the radio equipment.

Attenuation (dB)	R1 (Ω)	R2 (Ω)	R3(Ω)
1	2.875	2.875	433.3
2	5.731	5.731	215.2
3	8.55	8.55	141.96
4	11.31	11.31	104.8
5	14.01	14.01	82.24
6	16.67	16.67	66.67
7	19.12	19.12	55.80
8	21.53	21.53	47.31
10	25.97	25.97	35.14
12	29.92	29.92	26.81
15	34.9	34.9	18.36
20	40.91	40.91	10.10
25	44.67	44.67	5.641
30	46.9	46.9	3.165
35	48.25	48.25	1.779
40	49.01	49.01	1.0

Table A3.1: Details for theoretical T-network attenuators comprising three resistors R1, R2 and R3 are shown in Figure 84.

Referring to Figure 83
Assuming the attenuator is for 50Ω operation, that the load connected to the attenuator is a pure 50Ω resistance and RMS values are used for the voltage and current, then the current drawn by the attenuator is:

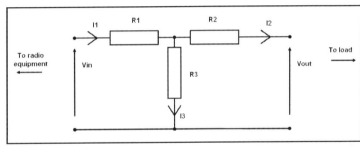

Figure 83: Concept of a theoretical T-network attenuator suitable for use with coaxial cables.

$$I1 \ (\text{amps}) = \frac{in}{50}$$

The power dissipated by R1 is given by

$$(I1)^2 \times R1$$

The current drawn by the load is:

$$I2 \ (\text{amps}) = \frac{V_{out}}{50\Omega}$$

The power dissipated by R2 is given by

$$(I2)^2 \times R2$$

The current flowing through R3 is:

$$I3 \ (\text{amps}) = I1 - I2$$

The power dissipated by R3 is given by

$$(I3)^2 \times R3$$

The power dissipated by resistors R1, R2 and R3 is the maximum which each resistor can be expected to handle. As a safety factor, it is suggested that resistors R1, R2 and R3 should have a power dissipation rating of double the power calculated. Resistors R1, R2 and R3 may also need to be a composite of several resistors to obtain the required value in ohms. Therefore, the power rating for each of the individual resistors used will also need to be taken into consideration.

References

[1] Telecommunication Principles for Final Certificate Volume 2. Chapter 10 Transmission Along Lines, by S.K. Knight. Published by Newes-Butterworths. 1978.

[2] Radio Systems III, by D.C. Green. Chapter 4 Transmission Lines. Published by Pitman. 1979.

[3] RSGB Radio Communication Handbook, 13th edition edited by Mike Browne, G3DIH. Section 1, Principles, page 1.17.

[4] Microwave and RF Design, A Systems Approach, by Michael Steer. Published by.SciTech Publishing Inc, Raleigh, NC, USA. Section 4.6.1, pages 180 to 184. 2010.

[5] ARRL Antenna Book for Radio Communications, 23rd edition edited by H. Ward Silver N0AX. Chapter 23, Transmission Lines, pages 23-3 to 23-10.

[6] RSGB Radio Communication Handbook, 13th edition edited by Mike Browne, G3DIH. Section 14, Transmission Lines, pages 14.2 to14.3.

[7] RSGB Radio Communication Handbook, 5th edition. Chapter 12 HF Antennas, pages 12.26 to 12.28.

[8] RSGB Radio Communication Handbook, 5th edition. Chapter 12 HF Antennas, pages 12.25.

[9] RSGB Radio Communication Handbook, 13th edition edited by Mike Browne, G3DIH. Section 15, Practical HF Antennas, pages 15.3 to 15.5.

[10] RSGB Radio Communication Handbook, 5th edition. Section 12, HF Antennas, page 12.59.

[11] RSGB Radio Communication Handbook, 13th edition edited by Mike Browne, G3DIH. Section 13, Antenna Basics and Construction, page 13.2.

[12] RSGB RadCom July 2017, Antennas column, pages 24 to 26. Mike Parkin, G0JMI.

[13] RSGB RadCom October 2019, Antennas column, pages 26 to 27. Mike Parkin, G0JMI.

[14] RSGB RadCom January 2019, Antennas column, pages 15 to 17. Mike Parkin, G0JMI.

[15] ARRL Antenna Handbook for Radio Communications, 23rd edition edited by H. Ward Silver N0AX. Chapter 23, Transmission Lines, Figure 23.21, page 23-20.

[16] RSGB RadCom May 2010, 'In Practice' Pages 38 to 40. Ian White, GM3SEK.

[17] RSGB Radio Communication Handbook, 13th edition edited by Mike Browne, G3DIH. Section 14, Transmission Lines, pages 14.13 to 14.15.

[18] RSGB VHF/UHF Manual 4th Edition, by G.R. Jessop, G6JP. Section 8 Antennas Pages 8.7 to 8.9 Figure 19. Published 1983.

[19] ARRL Antenna Book for Radio Communications, 23rd edition edited by H. Ward Silver N0AX. Chapter 2, Dipoles and Monopoles, page 2-11.

[20] ARRL, The Radio Amateur's Handbook, 53rd edition edited by Robert Myers, W1FBY. Chapter 20, Transmission Lines, page 579.

[21] RSGB Radio Communication Handbook, 13th edition edited by Mike Browne, G3DIH. Section 14, Transmission Lines, page 14.12.

[22] RSGB RadCom October 2018, Antennas column, pages 18 to 20. Mike Parkin, G0JMI.

[23] RSGB Microwave Handbook Volume 1, edited by M. Dixon, G3PFR. Chapter 5, Transmisison Lines and Components, pages 5.5 to 5.7. Published 1989.

[24] RSGB Radio Communication Handbook, 5th edition. Section 23, General Data, page 23.39.

[25] RSGB Radio Communication Handbook, 13th edition edited by Mike Browne, G3DIH. Appendix A: General Data, Page A.

[26] RSGB Radio Communication Handbook, 13th edition edited by Mike Browne, G3DIH. Section 14, Transmission Lines, page 14.10 to 14.11.

[27] RSGB RadCom July 2017, Antennas column, pages 24 26. Mike Parkin, G0JMI.

[28] RSGB RadCom June 1998, 'In Practice'. Ian White, GM 3SEK.

[29] RSGB RadCom June 2019, Antennas column, pages 18 20. Mike Parkin, G0JMI.

[30] Amphenol® RF website: https://www.amphenolrf.co connectors/uhf.html

[31] RSGB Radio Communication Handbook, 13th edition ited by Mike Browne, G3DIH, Section 14, Transmission Line pages14.4 to 14.7.

[32] Collins Concise Dictionary, HarperCollins Publishing, edition 1999. Page 721.

[33] ARRL, The Radio Amateur's Handbook, 53rd edition ited by Robert Myers, W1FBY. Chapter 2, Electrical Laws a Circuits, page 35.

[34] RSGB RadCom March 2018, Antennas column, pages 16 17. Mike Parkin, G0JMI.

[35] RSGB RadCom April 2018, Antennas column, pages 24 26. Mike Parkin, G0JMI.

[36] RSGB Radio Communication Handbook, 13th edition edit by Mike Browne, G3DIH, Section 14, Transmission Lines, pag 14.18 and 14.20 (charts used are amended versions for the ima nary scales above -/+ j100)

[37] RSGB, RadCom Centenary Issue, July 2013. An Effecti Multi-band Aerial, pages 32 to 33. Louis Varney, G5RV.

[38] RSGB HF Antenna Collection, Edited by Erwin Dav G4LQI. Chapter 1 Single-Element Horizontally Polarised Ante nas. Pages 9 to 13. 1991.

[39] MMANA-GAL basic V3.0.0.31, freeware antenna analyzi application. Original code by Makoto Mori JE3HHT. MMAN GAL basic and MMANA-GAL Pro by Alex Schewelew DL1PBD, and Igor Gontcharenko, DL2KQ. 1999 onwards.

[40] Microwaves, 2nd edition, by A.J. Daben Fuller. Chap 1 Transmission Lines, pages 11 to 13. Published by Pergam Press. 1979.

[41] Fundamentals of Electricity and Magnetism, by Arthur Kip. Chapter 12 Maxwell's Equations and Electromagnetic Wav pages 445 to 449. Published by McGraw-Hill Kogakusha Ltd. 196

[42] Supplement to the Post Office Electrical Engineers' Journ Vol. 71 Part 3 October 1978. Line Transmission C 1977, page 7

[43] Radio Systems III, by D.C. Green. Chapter 11, Wideband Li Radio Systems, page 208. Published by Pitman. 1979.

[44] Electrical Technology, 5th edition, by Edward Hughes. Chap 1, The Electric Circuit: Maximum Power Transfer, pages 12 to 1 Thevenin's theory, pages 18 to 22. Published by Longman Gro Ltd, London. 1977.

[45] RSGB VHF/UHF Manual 4th Edition, by G.R. Jessop, G6. Appendix, page A17. Published 1983.